This book is to be re
the last date st

D1633292

Caring for someone with a heart problem

Toni Battison

EWCASTLE-UNDER-LYME
COLLEGE LIBRARY

AGE
Concern

BOOKS

Newcastle Under Lyme College

DC025871

© 1999 Toni Battison
Published by Age Concern England
1268 London Road
London SW16 4ER

First Published 1999

Editor   Gillian Clarke
Production   Vinnette Marshall
Designed and typeset by GreenGate Publishing Services, Tonbridge, Kent
Printed in Great Britain by Bell & Bain Ltd, Glasgow

A catalogue record for this book is available from the British Library.

ISBN 0–86242–252–3

All rights reserved; no part of this work may be reproduced in any form, by mimeograph or any other means, without permission in writing from the publisher.

Whilst the advice and information contained in *Caring for someone with a heart problem* is believed to be true and accurate at the time of going to press, neither Age Concern England nor the author can accept any legal responsibility or liability for any errors or omissions that may be made.

Bulk orders

Age Concern England is pleased to offer customised editions of all its titles to UK companies, institutions or other organisations wishing to make a bulk purchase. For further information, please contact the Publishing Department at the address on this page. Tel: 0181-765 7200. Fax: 0181-765 7211. E-mail: addisom@ace.org.uk.

Contents

649.8 BAT
NEWCASTLE-UNDER-LYME
COLLEGE LIBRARY
0C025871

About the author

Toni Battison is a trained nurse who has had considerable experience working with older people and carers at different stages of her career. These many 'hats' include practical experience as a district nursing sister, planning health promotion programmes as a health promotion adviser and teaching health professionals as a lecturer for the Certificate in Health Education.

She has always been concerned about the need to support carers and patients, to help them get the best from local and national services. Her main interest for many years has focused on giving good quality information, as she believes strongly that people obtain great benefit from being able to help themselves. While working for the Cambridge and Huntingdon Health Authority she helped create an information centre, called The Health Shop, for patients and visitors at Addenbrooke's Hospital, and, with other carers, started the Telephone Information Line for Carers of Elderly People in the Cambridge area.

Toni has written a number of books, directories and teaching packs on topics promoting good health, and was a regular contributor to Radio Cambridgeshire while working as a health promotion adviser. Now retired from the NHS, she works as manager of a volunteer bureau as well as working freelance in health information.

Toni lives near Cambridge with her husband and mother, and has three grown-up daughters. She spent much time recently helping her mother care for her father, after he suffered a stroke, until he died at home. This time as a personal carer has given her a different perspective of caring that complements her professional experience.

Acknowledgements

The author thanks the many carers, friends and colleagues who contributed valuable help and advice towards the production of this book. In particular:

Joan Bragg, for sharing her feelings and memories abut Peter's illness;

Val Beamish, State Registered Dietitian;

Dr Sarah Brewer, medical writer;

Jill Briggs, Lead Practitioner for District Nurses, and Sally Feast, Senior Occupational Therapist, both from Lifespan Healthcare NHS Trust;

Beryl Sarsfield, Carers' Support Worker, Cambridgeshire Social Services;

Debrae Walsh, Senior Lecturer/Aromatherapist, Homerton College, Cambridge, School of Health Studies;

Gill Westland, Psychotherapist, Cambridge Body Psychotherapy Centre;

A J Geddes, Bendall & Sons, Solicitors;

Dr S G P Webster, Consultant Physician, Addenbrooke's NHS Trust;

The staff and volunteers at Directions Plus, Cambridge.

In addition I thank all the national organisations that offer information and support to carers in the broadest sense, whose materials have helped to inform and influence my thinking, and to the people at Age Concern for their support and advice throughout the stages of publication, especially Richard Holloway, Vinnette Marshall, Sue Ramsden (Age Concern Scotland) and Gillian Clarke.

Introduction

Most people know something about coronary heart disease (CHD), because a relative or friend is affected and because it is a topic of ill-health that is widely discussed in the media and society in general. Unfortunately, coronary heart disease is the greatest cause of ill-health and death throughout the western world today. According to the British Heart Foundation, in Britain alone it accounts for about half of all deaths each year – the north of England, Scotland and Northern Ireland topping the international league tables. Annually, almost 2 million people in the UK suffer from angina, and together the cardiovascular diseases kill around one-third of a million people.

These are difficult figures to grasp, and they make sombre reading if you are caring for someone who is suffering from a heart problem. The good news is that treatments and care nowadays are excellent and many people with heart problems are able to lead relatively normal lives; the outlook for future generations has also improved as the number of deaths linked to coronary heart disease continues to fall each year, particularly among younger people. Coronary heart disease (and its associated risk factors) is one of the main conditions included in the government's health promotion programme *The Health of the Nation*, which aims to reduce the level of ill-health and death in a number of key areas. The main targets for coronary heart disease are:

- To reduce the death rate in people under 65 by at least 40 per cent by the year 2000.
- To reduce the death rate in people aged 65–74 by at least 30 per cent by the year 2000.

Other targets relate to the risk factors for coronary heart disease, including changes or reduction in factors such as diet and nutrition, obesity, blood pressure and alcohol consumption.

The purpose of this book is to offer information, advice and support to people who care for someone with coronary heart disease and the associated problems of the circulatory system, and to provide an insight into some of the issues related to caring. Throughout the text there are quotes from people with heart disease and their carers and from health professionals; the names have been changed but they are real people. The person you are caring for may be a spouse, a relative or a friend but, for simplicity, they are referred to always as 'your relative'.

The Carers National Association has found that there are nearly 7 million carers in the UK. In simple terms, this means that one adult in seven is looking after someone who, because of ill-health or old age, can no longer maintain complete independence. The issues are no longer hidden, and the value to society of these non-professional carers is slowly being recognised. Acts of Parliament have been passed that create a firm base for pursuing the rights and needs of both carers and their dependants.

Carers are beginning to seek assistance but a survey carried out by the Carers National Association, *Still Battling?*, found that many people did not know that they are entitled to services and support. The survey concluded that 82 per cent of people questioned had not asked for an assessment of their ability to care.

> 'These issues must be addressed if we are to make the best use of the most precious of all resources in community care – the unpaid help, willingly given, of carers.' Carers National Association (*Still Battling?* 1997)

This book outlines what is available for carers through the statutory and voluntary organisations, and provides an introduction to a number of techniques and complementary therapies that will help you to cope with the caring situation. Unfortunately, there are shortfalls and gaps in most local authority and health services, and there are rarely answers and solutions to every question and problem! Nevertheless, sources of support are out there to help you cope with the hard work, the stress and the feelings of frustration, and enough information is available to make finding your way around the caring maze less difficult.

1 What do we mean by heart disease?

Heart disease, in everyday terms, means any problem that affects both the heart and the circulation. The most common illness, coronary heart disease (CHD), is recognised as the biggest cause of disability and death in the western world. Coronary heart disease is not a single illness affecting the heart itself, but is a term used to describe problems that occur in the arteries immediately surrounding the heart. The coronary arteries supply the heart with oxygen-rich blood. When these become narrowed or blocked, the lack of blood may cause the pain of angina. Complete blockage means that part of the heart muscle dies for lack of blood; this is a heart attack.

The person you care for may already have had a heart attack, or they may have angina or another less common problem affecting their heart or circulatory system. This chapter describes these problems in greater detail, starting with the structure of the heart and the circulatory system. Knowing how the heart works will help you and your relative to understand what has gone wrong and why some of the tests and treatments are necessary. As a result, you will both feel more confident about asking questions, which could help to make visits to the hospital or doctor less distressing.

The chapter also looks at some of the risk factors affecting other family members and offers some advice from a doctor and a carer about recovery after a major heart attack.

The structure and function of the heart

How does it work?

The heart is a bag of muscle about the size of a clenched fist that acts as two separate but interrelated pumps. It is divided into four sections (chambers), each separated by a strong dividing wall. The central wall between the left and right halves is normally unbroken, whilst the wall dividing the top chambers (atria) from the bottom chambers (ventricles) contains a one-way opening (valve) to allow the blood to pass through (figure 1). Each chamber is about the same size but the walls of the ventricles are much thicker than those of the atria because they have to work harder pumping blood away from the heart. The atria have less work to do because their function is to receive blood from the veins into the heart and pump it down to the ventricles. The valves stop the blood being pushed back in the wrong direction and can be one of the parts of the heart that become diseased and fail (valvular heart disease is described in the section 'Heart valve replacement' on p 22).

The blood is carried through the body by arteries and veins. Each pumping action of the heart is triggered by an electrical impulse that sets off a sequence of events making up one heart beat: first the atria contract, then the ventricles, followed by a resting phase.

How does the blood flow?

Think of a heart as being like the pump in a central heating system: water cannot get to the furthest radiator unless it is pushed there. The main function of the heart is to pump blood rich in oxygen to the muscles and organs all over the body. To do this the right atrium receives exhausted (de-oxygenated) blood, which is immediately pumped to the ventricle below. From here the strong muscle walls pump the de-oxygenated blood to the lungs where waste gas (carbon dioxide) is exchanged through the walls of the fine blood vessels for fresh oxygen. The newly oxygenated blood is carried directly back to the left side of the heart where the same

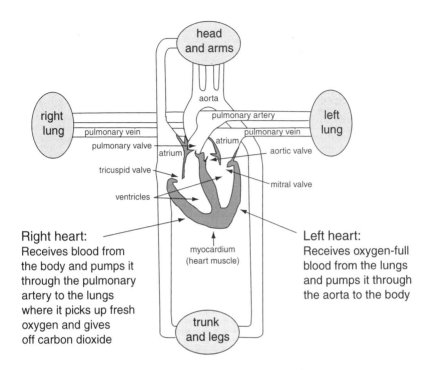

Fig. 1 Diagram of the structure of the heart (Redrawn by permission of the British Heart Foundation)

pumping process pushes it to the extremities of the body. Oxygen, carried via the red blood cells, is then released along the way, bringing vital energy to every living tissue in the body. This demand for energy is constant but variable according to how active you are; for example, the need is much lower when you are asleep than when walking up a hill.

Just as water pipes in the central heating system may get blocked with lime deposits, so may the arteries become narrowed or blocked with fatty deposits. The narrower the arteries, the less room there is for blood to flow. When a person is suffering from coronary heart disease, the blood supply to the heart is poor. This means there is insufficient oxygen to meet the increased demands on the heart during exercise; this causes the pain of angina.

Fact box

- An average heart beats 70 times per minute, or 100,000 times per day.
- An average heart pumps 80ml of blood with each beat, or 8,000 litres per day.
- A heart valve opens and closes about 40 million times a year.
- About 20 per cent of adults in the UK have high blood pressure.
- Nearly 2 million people in the UK suffer from angina each year.
- About 330,000 people in the UK have a heart attack each year.
- Over 15,000 people have coronary surgery procedures in the UK each year.
- About 1 in 7 men and 1 in 17 women in the UK die of coronary heart disease before the age of 75.

Sources: all but the final entry: *Beating Heart Disease the Natural Way* by Dr Sarah Brewer; final entry: British Heart Foundation

What are the risk factors?

Fiona, *a doctor*

'Family history cannot be changed, but otherwise the risks of heart disease can be reduced.'

The chances of developing coronary heart disease will depend on a range of contributing circumstances known as 'risk factors'. The rate at which it gets worse also depends on these factors. The risk factors linked to coronary heart disease are:

- family history of heart disease;
- smoking cigarettes;
- increasing age;
- untreated high blood pressure;
- diet high in saturated (animal) fat;

- abnormally high levels of blood fats (eg cholesterol);
- being overweight or obese;
- taking insufficient exercise;
- drinking large amounts of alcohol;
- being male – until middle age; then the risk rate for post-menopausal women equals that for men;
- having diabetes that cannot easily be controlled.

Although the ageing process cannot be slowed down and family history cannot be altered, many of the other factors *can* be changed to improve general health and reduce the future risk of heart disease. Chapter 3 offers ideas and suggestions to help you make improvements in life-style.

> **Eric, a doctor**
>
> 'It's never too late to improve your life-style.'

What can go wrong?

High blood pressure (hypertension)

High blood pressure affects about 10–20 per cent of the adult population but, unfortunately, remains undiagnosed in many people until a more serious illness requires medical attention. Although it is the forerunner of many heart attacks or strokes, it rarely causes symptoms even when dangerously high.

When the pressure of blood is measured (BP: blood pressure) the reading is affected by several elements: the volume of blood and its stickiness (viscosity), the strength of the heart's contraction (pushing the blood along), the rate of the beat and the diameter, elasticity and resistance of the arterial walls. It is entirely normal for blood pressure to be raised after physical activity and to differ throughout the day but a person with hypertension will have blood pressure readings that are high even at rest. Hypertension is more common in men than in women and tends to increase during middle age.

Blood pressure is usually measured on the arteries of the arm by inflating a special cuff that is wrapped round the upper arm. The cuff is attached to an instrument that gives a reading of two numbers: the higher number (systolic pressure) relates to the pressure in the circulation as the heart contracts and pushes blood into the aorta; the lower number (diastolic pressure) indicates the pressure in the system as the heart relaxes between beats. The average reading for a healthy young adult is 120/80 while at rest, but a person in middle age could register a pressure of 150/90. It is likely that treatment would be started if the blood pressure regularly exceeded 160/95.

The risk of raised blood pressure is commonly linked with factors that can also cause coronary heart disease (eg obesity, a family history, lack of exercise, smoking cigarettes and high consumption of alcohol). In particular, it is thought to be directly related to the total amount of salt in the diet. Reducing their intake of salt to lower the systolic blood pressure could also help to reduce the risk of stroke or coronary heart disease for many people.

High blood pressure puts extra strain on the arterial wall linings and speeds up the development of atherosclerosis (see below). In a small number of people, raised blood pressure is caused by an illness, such as kidney disease, and will be treated accordingly.

Atherosclerosis

'Atherosclerosis' is the medical term used to describe the problem caused by 'furring up' of the arteries. It starts at an early age, and several factors contribute to the slow, thickening process that in many people leads to angina and possibly a heart attack. At first, general wear and tear occurs so the artery walls become less smooth. Then fatty materials (cholesterol) produced naturally by the body and also taken in through a high fat diet stick to the walls, leaving patchy, porridge-like deposits that narrow the passage-way. In some people damage to the arteries is made worse by:

■ chemicals in cigarette smoke;
■ high blood pressure;

■ a family tendency to produce excess cholesterol;
■ diabetes.

Lack of exercise and stress also play a part and eventually the artery loses its elasticity and becomes more fibrous. This is known as 'hardening' of the arteries, a term commonly used to describe the state of the blood vessels.

Will the problem get worse?

Many long-term problems can result from atherosclerosis as it builds up slowly for many years, affecting all parts of the body. The most common are:

■ chronic (long-term) high blood pressure;
■ permanent damage to organs such as the kidneys;
■ poor peripheral circulation, particularly in the legs;
■ gradual loss of brain cells, leading to vascular dementia.

One sign of a serious problem is often the pain of mild angina, because the fatty 'plaques' in the artery walls restrict the flow of blood to the heart. If the plaques crack or become roughened, a blood clot forms over the damaged tissue; this process is called thrombosis, and 'thrombus' is another word for 'clot'. This may block the coronary artery and starve part of the heart muscle of blood, causing a heart attack. If a piece of clot breaks off, it can float in the blood until it wedges in a narrow blood vessel. A travelling clot is called an 'embolus' and the process is 'embolism'.

A clot from the leg can travel to the lungs, causing the dangerous condition of 'pulmonary embolism'. Thrombosis or embolism in the brain arteries causes a stroke. Thrombosis can occur elsewhere in the body. In the leg, thrombosis cases redness, pain and swelling.

Varicose veins

Varicose veins are veins that have become stretched and dilated (widened) out of proportion to the amount of blood they carry. Veins vary greatly in thickness in different people, and even in different parts of the same vein. Therefore dilation will depend on the structure of the vein wall and any damage to the surrounding tissue (eg after an injury). These blood vessels are subject to degenerative and inflammatory changes from the late teens onwards, and are prevalent in women, particularly during pregnancy. The most common sites to be affected are the inner side of the lower leg, knee and thigh, the lower end of the bowel (haemorrhoids, piles) and the testicles (varicocele).

It is estimated that about two-thirds of adults in the UK have varicose veins; some people are more prone than others owing to a combination of genetic make-up and occupational risks. Jobs that require long periods of standing, with little opportunity for vigorous muscle action, put a great strain on the veins and fail to provide the pumping action necessary to exert the muscle contractions that push the blood back to the heart. After a vein has begun to dilate, its walls become weaker and have poorer valve control; so the weight of blood pressing down in the veins increases and the symptoms worsen to the point that surrounding veins become affected as they take on a greater workload.

Symptoms of varicose veins are:

- bulging, 'knotted' veins at the surface of the legs (or other affected area of the body);
- fatigue on exertion;
- aching, particularly after standing;
- swelling of the ankles.

Complications can occur that may need immediate or long-term treatment. If the area surrounding the vein becomes red, inflamed and painful (thrombophlebitis), it is important to seek urgent medical advice, because a blood clot can easily form and cause a blockage in the vein. The clot could then become infected or parts might break away and become lodged elsewhere in a critical area of the body. In the long term it is important to prevent breakdown of the surrounding skin, because the resulting varicose ulcer can be difficult and tedious to treat.

Treatment of varicose veins

Treatment will depend on the nature and severity of the problem. Inflammation of the vein and surrounding tissues may require immediate antibiotic drugs. The doctor may then prescribe support stockings, an injection into the vein to shrink and close the affected area or surgical removal of the diseased veins. A number of self-help strategies are worth trying to ease the symptoms:

- if it is necessary to stand for long periods, keep the leg and calf muscles moving;
- if it is necessary to sit for long periods, keep the leg and calf muscles moving or get up and walk around;
- lie down and rest when possible with the legs raised above heart level;
- don't become overweight – or reduce weight levels if already overweight;
- don't become constipated, as this increases pressure on the abdominal and rectal veins, reducing their capacity to take blood flow away from the lower half of the body.

Peripheral vascular disease

Peripheral vascular disease occurs as a direct result of the 'hardening' and 'furring up' of the arteries, and causes unpleasant leg cramps when increased activity calls for additional oxygen to the muscles (see p 69). When the blood supply is reduced, exercise will cause severe pain, which stops at rest – a condition known as 'intermittent claudication'. If the blood supply is very poor, the pain can occur even when the person is resting. If your relative complains of painful leg cramps, be sure that the doctor is aware of this because high blood pressure and diabetes are known causes. People with severe peripheral vascular disease are at risk of developing leg ulcers, so take care to prevent skin damage from broken toe nails or from knocking against furniture.

Treatment of peripheral vascular disease

Treatment is by medication, surgical by-pass or stretching of the artery at the site of the blockage.

Angina

Joan

'Peter suffered from angina. It wasn't too bad at first, affecting him only in cold weather, but even this made a difference to our lives – we became limited in what we could do as a couple. I didn't want to do things alone.'

Angina is the name given to pain or 'tightness' that starts in the chest and spreads upwards and outwards, affecting mainly the left side of the upper body. It is most painful in the neck, the jaw and down the left arm. The symptoms can vary in severity from temporary discomfort to a severe, crushing pain that makes the person feel breathless and sick. It occurs when the condition atherosclerosis (described on p 6) prevents sufficient oxygen reaching the heart muscle. The shortage of oxygen is felt when the heart is asked to work harder, and is most likely to occur during:

■ increased activity or exertion;
■ anxiety and emotional stress;
■ exposure to cold and/or strong wind;
■ digestion of a heavy meal, when the blood supply is naturally diverted to the stomach.

Occasionally, people experience angina when resting or asleep. Doctors believe this is caused by a spasm (contraction) in the coronary artery that worsens the already poor blood supply. This type of angina is more unstable because the attacks of pain tend to vary in intensity and duration; it should never be ignored.

Fiona, a doctor

'If you are worried, worry the GP!'

The first signs of angina-like pain should always be investigated by a doctor, particularly if the feelings of tightness and breathlessness are relieved by resting. Many people treat the early symptoms as indigestion and delay visiting their doctor. It is better to seek early help and reassurance than to try to 'self-medicate' and allow the disease to progress to a stage where surgery may be necessary or, worse, a heart attack occurs. If the symptoms are severe, regard the condition as an emergency. Dial 999 for immediate help, as paramedical teams are trained to give treatment on the spot. The person who is ill should never attempt to drive to hospital. Angina is not a heart attack but it may be a warning sign that the person is at risk of having one.

Joan

'I was always aware of the angina and wondered if it would play up – it was always at the back of my mind.'

Diagnosis of angina

The doctor will make a diagnosis of angina based on a number of factors:

- the symptoms describing the pain: what it feels like, how long it lasts, when and how often it occurs;
- a review of the person's medical history, including any family history;
- a physical examination to check heart beat and chest sounds;
- various tests.

The tests (see p 14) are carried out to help the doctor understand the state of the heart and surrounding arteries. They will also rule out conditions with similar signs and symptoms that cause pains in the chest (eg problems in the digestive system or severe anxiety).

Eric, *a doctor*

'If someone is slowing down, has a pain or is more breathless, don't assume it's their age – seek advice from a GP.'

Treatment of angina

The treatment given will depend on the severity of the angina, and may need to be reviewed if the condition of the heart and surrounding arteries changes. The GP and hospital clinic will

11

check the situation as often as is necessary. The two main courses of treatment are medication and surgery. To be effective, each will need to be supported by changes in general life-style and some adjustments may have to be made. Recovery rates are good and having angina should not stop your relative from living a full and active life. Chapter 3 deals more fully with ways to reduce the risk factors and thus help to prevent further attacks.

Joan

'It did affect Peter in some ways because he got frustrated. I would tell him not to fuss about things that would probably sort themselves out. He changed his hobbies a bit and did more indoors and less in the garden.'

Heart attack

The medical term for a heart attack is 'myocardial infarction', meaning damage to an organ (in this case the heart) caused by an interruption of the blood supply. Another term commonly used is 'coronary thrombosis', which takes its name from the action that occurs – a blockage to the blood supply of the heart caused by a blood clot lodged in a coronary artery. The severity of a heart attack depends on how much and where the heart muscle is affected. Damage to the conducting system may mean the heart beat cannot be co-ordinated; the heart is then unable to work properly, and may stop, causing sudden death. Very severe damage to large amounts of heart muscle may also be fatal.

The long-term build-up of arterial deposits, which can lead to a heart attack, are described in the sections on 'Atherosclerosis' (p 6) and 'Angina' (p 10). A heart attack can happen at any time, whether the person is resting or highly active.

Recognising a heart attack

A heart attack is a serious medical emergency, so never delay in calling an ambulance. A single tablet of aspirin is a useful immediate treatment that can be given at home, provided the person is conscious and is able to swallow without difficulty. If the following symptoms are present, dial 999:

- pain – crushing, squeezing, pressing – starting in the central chest and radiating outward into the neck, shoulders and arms; unlike angina it does not ease with rest;
- paleness with cold sweats;
- breathlessness;
- palpitations (unusually rapid and strong heart beat);
- nausea and vomiting;
- faintness or impaired consciousness.

Paramedical ambulance teams are trained to give excellent care for a suspected heart attack and will start emergency treatment before your relative reaches hospital. Make your relative lie down, and stay with them for reassurance and to check their condition. If they stop breathing, give mouth-to-mouth resuscitation. Cardiac massage should be given *only* by a person trained in the technique.

Fiona, *a doctor*

'The sooner the diagnosis of the heart attack is made, the better – the sooner treatment is started, the more likely it is to be effective.'

Diagnosis and hospital care

Someone with a suspected heart attack will be taken either directly to a coronary care unit (CCU) or to an accident and emergency (A&E) centre, depending on bed space and hospital facilities. Initially, a diagnosis is made from a description of the pain; tests (see p 14) are made at a later stage to confirm the preliminary diagnosis and the extent of damage to the heart muscle. Immediate treatment will include:

- various drugs (usually given through a vein in the arm) to relieve pain, dissolve the blood clot, regulate the heart beat and bring about sedation;
- oxygen to help breathing;
- connection to an ECG (electrocardiograph) machine to monitor the heart's electrical waves;

- blood tests to detect changes in body chemistry;
- initial bed rest, leading to gradually increased activity.

The care of patients differs according to their individual needs and the practice favoured by different consultants but all treatment works towards early mobility and discharge from hospital. Chapter 3 deals more fully with changes in life-style that may be necessary after a heart attack.

What tests and treatments are given?

Diagnostic tests for heart conditions

The tests described here are the main ones used to inform doctors about the state of the heart and circulatory system, to help make a diagnosis and to decide upon appropriate treatment.

- **Electrocardiogram (ECG)** Small electrodes are attached to several points on the body to record any abnormalities in the electrical impulses of the heart. (The test is completely painless.) Patients who have had a heart attack have their ECG monitored continuously in the early stages. (Continuous monitoring is usually with a TV monitor rather than a paper recording.) The readings help to assess the amount of muscle damage and the exact area where it occurred.
- **Blood tests** These are done to detect abnormal levels of body chemicals in the blood, indicating that a heart attack has taken place. The levels of enzymes (chemicals released by dead heart muscle) can be used to gauge the amount of damage.
- **Angiocardiography** This technique is used when a more detailed picture of the heart and coronary arteries is necessary, for example before heart surgery. Liquid that shows up on X-ray is injected into the circulation, and outlines the coronary arteries as it flows through them. This can be seen on a TV monitor, and narrowing or blockage by atheroma or clot can be identified.
- **Doppler ultrasound** This test uses high-frequency sound waves to determine the speed and direction of blood as it flows through the heart and circulatory system.

Medication (drugs) to treat heart conditions

Eric, a doctor

'If you don't understand about any treatment, ask – again and again, if necessary.'

The information given here is intended only as a brief outline of the main medicines used to treat different heart problems so that you and your relative understand why medication is so important and what effects it can have. It can be confusing for a lay person but the words 'drug' and 'medicine' mean the same thing in medical terms. Some drugs must be taken regularly to prevent a condition getting worse (eg the long-term use of anticoagulants to 'thin' the blood) whereas others are taken only when symptoms develop, such as the pain of angina. It is important to check the information given on the label, and never stop using a drug without medical advice. If you are unsure about any aspect of medication your relative is taking, it's best to check with their own doctor or ask the pharmacist at the chemist's shop.

Although there seem to be many drugs in use for the treatment of heart disease, in reality there are only a few main groups (described below). There are two main reasons for this abundance of drugs:

■ Any one drug may be available in several variations, which enables doctors to prescribe the best 'match' for the person's symptoms; it may take several attempts to find the one that gives the best results with the least side (unwanted) effects.

■ Different manufacturers give the same basic drug a different colour and trade name. Think of medicine like coffee on a supermarket shelf – the names and the packaging are different but the granules are the same!

How do drugs get into the system?

There are three main ways to give drugs. The most common route is through the mouth, as tablets, capsules or liquid; some drugs work better by being injected into the blood stream; and occasionally they are given via the skin. The various methods are:

- **Aerosol**   The drug is sprayed directly onto or under the tongue, where it will be absorbed quickly.
- **Buccal**   The tablet is placed between the upper lip and gum, and is a much slower method of absorption – four to six hours.
- **Intramuscular**   An injection is given deep into a muscle, usually the buttock or thigh.
- **Intravenous**   The liquid drug is injected into a vein, rapidly by syringe or slowly by a drip feed. Drugs are given this way to dissolve blood clots in the case of a suspected heart attack.
- **Self-adhesive patches**   This method, which gives a slow absorption of the drug, is sometimes used in the prevention of angina.
- **Subcutaneous**   An injection is made just under the surface of the skin. The anticoagulant drug heparin is sometimes given by this method.
- **Sublingual**   A tablet is placed under the tongue where it dissolves and is absorbed quickly into the blood stream, going directly to the heart without being destroyed by the liver first. This method is used for easing the pain of angina, and means that the drug can easily be taken without liquid.

What types of drugs are used most commonly?

The main drugs used in the treatment of heart problems fall into several groups, some people needing a combination of medication to produce the best results.

Drug treatments for angina

Nitrates (eg glyceryl trinitrate: GTN)   are used very effectively in the treatment of angina. They relax the walls of arteries and veins to allow an increased flow of blood and reduce the amount of work the heart has to do. Side effects include headaches, dizziness and 'flushing' of the face.

Beta blockers (eg propranolol)   are used to slow down and lower the force of the heart beat. They are particularly good during exercise and in times of stress, because they block the passage of hormones such as adrenaline that stimulate the nervous system, making the heart work harder. Side effects include tiredness, fatigue, cold and tingling in the hands and feet and, occasionally, nausea and diarrhoea, skin rashes and nightmares. They are not suitable for people with asthma, as they may bring on an attack.

Calcium channel blockers (eg nifedipine)   act in a more complicated way. Calcium is a mineral essential for the work of all body cells connected with muscle contraction. These drugs block the level of calcium entering a cell and help to control the strength of the contraction and relax the muscle wall. This in turn increases the blood supply and reduces the work of the heart. Side effects include headaches, arrhythmia (abnormal heart rhythm), swollen ankles and 'flushing' of the face.

Potassium channel openers (eg nicorandil)   are a new class of drugs. They work mainly by dilating (widening) the artery walls to increase blood supply to the heart muscle and by triggering a natural process that allows heart cells a brief rest when they are lacking in oxygen. This last action can prevent cells dying from shortage of oxygen, thus reducing the risks of angina and heart attack.

Drug treatments for high blood pressure

Diuretics (eg bendrofluazide)   are used mainly to reduce the amount of fluid and salt in the body – this in turn lowers blood pressure and subsequently the work of the heart. They may also help to dilate small arteries. Some diuretics cause too much potassium to be lost from the body. This can be harmful, so a potassium supplement or a change of drug may be needed to correct the problem. Side effects can include weakness, dizziness, faintness, nausea and vomiting, and are linked to an increased risk of developing gout if uric acid levels in the blood are raised. Certain diuretics can affect blood sugar control, so this type (thiazide) should not be taken by anyone with diabetes. People who take diuretics should be careful about the amount of salt in their diet because this can counteract their effects; a dietitian or the practice nurse can give advice about this.

ACE (Angiotensin-Converting Enzyme) inhibitors are used to reduce the production of the angiotensin-converting enzyme (a chemical), which constricts blood vessels. When combined with a diuretic, these drugs increase the blood supply to the kidneys and help the flow of urine, although this can act in reverse if the kidneys are already diseased. ACE inhibitors are generally well tolerated by most users. Side effects include a cough, dizziness, skin rash and impaired taste.

Alpha blockers (eg prazosin) act to reduce blood pressure by dilating arteries and veins. They are used if the drugs mentioned above are not successful alone. Side effects include too great a fall in blood pressure (especially after the first dose), tiredness, dizziness and weakness.

Beta blockers and calcium channel blockers are discussed on pp 16–17, in the section 'Drug treatments for angina'.

Drug treatments for dissolving and preventing blood clots

Streptokinase is used only in an emergency for quick intravenous action after a heart attack, to break up a clot. It is not used if there is a risk of bleeding from other parts of the body, for example soon after an operation.

Heparin is an anticoagulant, used to prevent further clotting taking place. It is given urgently by intravenous injection, or subcutaneously (under the skin) for a short course of less urgent treatment.

Warfarin is given by mouth as a long-term anticoagulant to prevent clots forming. It is commonly used for people who have valvular heart disease, especially those who have been given a replacement heart valve. Warfarin is also used to treat deep vein thrombosis, to help prevent blood clots moving to the lungs. People who take anticoagulants should always carry an identification card because of the increased risk of internal bleeding. The doctor or pharmacist should always be told that your relative is taking an anticoagulant if other treatment is being prescribed: the action of anticoagulants can be affected by many other drugs, including antibiotics and aspirin.

Aspirin has fairly recently been recognised as an effective treatment in the prevention of blood clots and is now widely used for people who have coronary heart disease or who have had a stroke. However, it is not wise for healthy people to take aspirin as a long-term precaution, because it can cause digestive problems and occasionally triggers asthmatic attacks.

Drug treatments for abnormal rhythm of the heart and heart failure

Several groups of drugs are used to regulate and control disturbances in the normal heart beat, often in a combination to produce the best effect. They work by making the beat stronger or by reducing resistance in the arteries.

Arrhythmics (eg amiodarone) are used when the heart rhythm is seriously erratic. Their use must be monitored carefully because they frequently give unpleasant side effects, including headaches, 'flushing' of the face, dizziness, stomach disorders and, in some people, affecting the lungs, liver, skin colour and thyroid gland.

Beta blockers and calcium channel blockers are discussed on pages 16–17.

Digoxin is the main drug used to slow the heart when it is beating fast and irregularly (atrial fibrillation). It is especially useful when the heart is struggling to function in this abnormal rhythm, as the drug strengthens the heart's contraction as well as slowing its rate. The main side effects are loss of appetite, vomiting and disturbance of heart rhythm. It may be necessary to do blood tests to measure the amount of digoxin in the person's blood to make sure that the dose is just right.

Drug treatments for lowering cholesterol

High levels of cholesterol are treated first by adjusting the amount eaten in the diet (see Chapter 3). The second method, treatment by drugs, is used if the levels remain high after dietary changes and the person is at risk from coronary heart disease. There are several types of drugs commonly used to lower blood cholesterol levels.

Resins (eg colestipol) work by stopping bile acids being re-absorbed into the gut. The liver responds by breaking down more cholesterol into bile acids, which are then passed out as waste products. Resins are effective but unpleasant to take because large amounts of granules must be swallowed. Side effects include digestive problems such as nausea and vomiting, constipation or diarrhoea and flatulence (wind).

Statins (eg simvastatin) reduce cholesterol levels by slowing down its production in the liver. Side effects include discomfort in muscles that can be felt as non-cardiac chest pain, flatulence (wind), constipation and fatigue.

Fibrates (eg ciprofibrate) work by affecting the way the liver acts on cholesterol. They are not as effective as other drugs at reducing cholesterol levels and can cause muscular pain, hair loss and stomach upsets; in some people they trigger the formation of gall stones through excess excretion of cholesterol into the bile.

Nicotinic acid derivatives (eg nicofuranose) work in two ways: by inhibiting the breakdown of stored body fat and by slowing down the production of fats in the liver. Their side effects include dilation of the blood vessels, causing dizziness, headaches and 'flushing' of the face; the side effects are severe enough to limit their usefulness.

Probucol is the only one of its type. Its action is not accurately known but it seems to encourage the liver to break down more cholesterol by increasing the excretion of bile acids in the stools. Side effects are mainly felt in the gut, causing flatulence (wind), abdominal pain and diarrhoea.

Surgical treatments

Insertion of a pacemaker

Each heart beat is triggered by a tiny electrical signal (spark) that sends an electrical impulse along a conducting system (the equivalent of wires) to the pumping chambers of the heart. The sparking system should ensure that the heart beats regularly, but in some people the electrical system ceases to function correctly. The fault may lie in the initial sparking centre or through a failure in transmission of the impulse. In either case the pumping chambers are not usually affected. This is often due to coronary artery disease, though sometimes no cause may be found; a few people are born with an abnormality of conduction. The effect of the abnormality is failure to co-ordinate the contraction of the chambers. In severe cases the heart may be unable to pump blood effectively, and this can cause sudden death.

Diagnosis of an electrical fault

Symptoms that indicate there is a malfunction in the electrical system, causing heart rhythm disturbance (cardiac arrhythmia), can vary quite considerably. Some people may have defects that do not give any symptoms whilst others experience dizziness and blackouts when the heart misses beats for short periods. A diagnosis is made from:

- a description of the signs and symptoms;
- an ECG test (if a single test does not pick up a fault, a 24-hour monitor may be set up).

Fitting the pacemaker

An artificial electrical trigger, called a pacemaker, can be fitted to stimulate the heart to beat normally. A slim wire, called an electrode, is introduced into the heart via a vein in the shoulder or neck and then attached to a small box containing the pacemaker. The box holds long-lasting batteries and the electronic circuits that control the on and off switch to trigger the heart beat. If the underlying condition is likely to improve with treatment (eg after a heart attack), a temporary pacemaker is fitted and carried outside the body. If the condition is unlikely to improve, a more permanent pacemaker is fitted – placed under the skin, usually below the collar bone.

After-care

Richard

'My wife and I felt nervous at first and she was very careful about giving me a hug but we gradually relaxed. Making a few jokes about the extra weight and alien bodies helped to ease the tension.'

Immediately after a pacemaker has been inserted it is important to take care of the wound and avoid introducing any infection or undue stress to the area. Any signs of redness or swelling should be reported promptly. Your relative's doctor will advise about getting back to normal: most activities can be resumed after about a month, including exercise, driving and sexual contact. The pacemaker will be checked at the outpatients clinic at regular intervals, more often in the early stages until everyone is happy with the progress.

When you are caring for someone with a pacemaker, try to forget that it exists! In practice pacemakers rarely go wrong, the batteries last for up to 10 years and most modern electronic equipment, unless it is malfunctioning, should not cause any interference with the pacemaker. The wisest move you can make is to check that your relative carries a card giving all personal details about the pacemaker.

Heart valve replacement

What goes wrong?

The valves in the heart stop the blood from flowing backwards. Valvular problems may either be congenital (present at birth) or occur because the valves become diseased through illness or degeneration. In many older people the problem stems from an attack of rheumatic fever, a complication of a throat infection, suffered in childhood before the days of antibiotic treatment. The illness causes the valves to become weak and deformed. Any of the main valves can be affected but it tends to be the mitral and aortic valves, which are most prone to deterioration because they have to work the hardest. The mitral valve prevents the back-flow of blood between the upper and lower chambers on the left side of the heart, and the aortic valve does the same job where blood is pumped from the lower left chamber to go to the lungs. A diseased valve becomes constricted and weak, causing a number of problems:

- extra strain is placed on the heart to push the blood through a narrower channel;
- the muscle walls thicken to compensate;
- blood dams up, causing congestion;
- blood leaks backwards through the weakened valves;
- fluid builds up in the lower half of the body, particularly in the abdomen and ankles, because of the problems caused by the harder work needed to pump the congested blood.

People with this condition are short of breath on exercise and sometimes on lying down in bed at night. They may also complain of tiredness and cough, occasionally producing blood. Clots may form in the malfunctioning heart and travel as emboli to the brain, where they cause a stroke.

Valve surgery

If the effects of a congenital condition are severe, surgical treatment will be necessary at an early stage in life. However, if rheumatic fever was the original cause of the deterioration, the need for treatment may not arise until much later in life. While the condition is not giving cause for concern, regular checks involving an ECG and a chest X-ray are sufficient to monitor the situation. If there is a deterioration, drug treatment may be started to relieve the congestion, reduce the work of the heart and regulate the heart beat; this could be supplemented with a minor surgical procedure to stretch the mitral valve with a balloon device. Surgery is often recommended before the symptoms become severe and damage to the heart is irreparable.

The need for surgery is most common in the mitral valve. Abnormal valves can be either repaired or replaced. Replacement valves may be artificial mechanical devices or biological transplants from humans or pigs. Which is chosen depends on the characteristics of the individual and the surgeon's opinion as to which will give the best outcome. There are a few minor differences in the two versions:

■ a mechanical valve clicks but a biological valve is silent;
■ a mechanical valve tends to create clots, so anticoagulant drugs must be taken permanently;
■ a biological valve requires anticoagulant drugs to be taken for a short period while it settles in;
■ if a biological valve is used, a second operation could be necessary after 10–15 years (a mechanical valve lasts much longer). The risk of this must be weighed against the tedium of taking daily anticoagulant drugs and the need for regular checks at the outpatient anticoagulant clinic.

After-care

The long-term prospects after replacement surgery are generally excellent. Patients will be advised individually about diet, exercise and, if appropriate, returning to work. It is important to guard against undue risk of infection, because replacement heart valves are more susceptible to this. In particular, infections can arise from bacteria that live in the mouth, so a high standard of dental care is necessary. Infection is especially likely after dental treatment or minor surgery. This dangerous complication can be prevented by taking antibiotics to 'cover' the procedure, so it is very important that the person tells the dentist or surgeon about the valve replacement.

By-pass surgery

Joan

'Peter had a heart attack four years after the angina started and he was admitted into hospital for a by-pass operation within two weeks.'

This is now a common procedure carried out to replace coronary arteries that have become blocked by a build-up of fatty substances. The surgeon creates a by-pass to allow fresh blood to flow through the coronary arteries, around the blockage. This is done by grafting in a blood vessel from another part of the patient's own body to create free-flowing routes in as many coronary arteries as necessary; from one to four is normal, depending on the level of disease.

After-care

Joan

'The operation was fine and the hospital staff were good but follow-up was not so well organised. Looking back, I think we should have asked more questions but at the time we didn't know what to expect. Peter did get some continuing pain.'

This operation is generally successful, especially in people without heart muscle damage from heart attacks. Untreated heart vessels and the graft itself may 'fur up' again, though, if the risk factors for atheroma are not dealt with.

Balloon angioplasty

This relatively new technique is used to stretch the coronary artery in many patients with coronary heart disease. A long, fine tube is inserted into an artery in the groin and manoeuvred into position at the site of the blocked coronary artery. When correctly placed, the tip of the tube is inflated under high pressure in order to create a wider passage in the artery to allow an increased blood flow.

Inflammation of the heart

Inflammation or an infection in various parts of the heart is less common nowadays because treatments, particularly antibiotics and steroids, are readily available. The three main conditions are:

- **Endocarditis** – literally, an infection of the heart lining, including the *heart valves*. It usually occurs in valves that are already abnormal. People who know they have damaged (or replacement) heart valves are advised to take special care with dental hygiene; they also should tell their dentist or surgeon about this, as they will need to take antibiotics to prevent endocarditis if they undergo dental treatment or surgery.
- **Myocarditis** – an infection of the *heart muscle*, which can develop after a severe attack of a viral illness with flu-like symptoms. Fortunately, this condition is very rare.
- **Pericarditis** – an infection of the *covering of the heart*, which can become inflamed after a heart attack or through a viral infection, causing pain and a general feeling of being unwell. As with myocarditis, the condition is rare.

Conclusion

This chapter has given basic information to help you and your relative understand how the heart and circulation work and has described some of the common conditions affecting many people today. The information has been technical in places, but knowing more about how the heart works will help you to understand why your relative has been ill. Tests are a necessary part of the diagnostic process and can be a frightening and unpleasant experience, particularly for someone who is feeling unwell, but many treatments cannot be started until the doctor has a clearer picture of the nature and extent of the problem.

As a carer you will probably accompany your relative to see the doctor, so it is vital that you also understand what is happening, to boost your confidence and improve the quality of care you provide. Most people in this situation feel anxious, so you are not alone if you find these visits daunting. Just remember that it's quite all right to ask questions about any aspect of the heart problem or care that you don't understand.

This chapter has also looked at some of the risk factors affecting other family members. If there seems to be a family history of heart disease, other family members should be aware of this and seek medical advice from an early age. Future chapters will help you and your relative make positive changes to daily living and help you think about your role and responsibility as a carer.

For more *i*nformation

i The British Heart Foundation publishes the Heart Information Series – a range of booklets on all problems and treatments relating to heart disease (address on p 164).

i The Coronary Prevention Group works towards the prevention of death and disability from heart disease, and provides a range of information leaflets, a newsletter and reading list (address on p 166).

i The 'Family Doctor' booklets *Understanding Cholesterol and Heart Disease* and *Understanding Blood Pressure* are available from most pharmacist/chemist shops.

i The Family Heart Association provides information on coronary heart disease and its management, including a 24-hour cholesterol and diet helpline and medical and nutritional advice (address on p 168).

i *High Blood Pressure* by Dr Sarah Brewer, published by Thorsons.

i PatientWise publishes a series of factsheets providing medical and health information for patients; they are available only through GPs and patient information centres – ask for details at your doctor's surgery.

i The Stroke Association works towards the prevention of chest, heart and stroke illnesses and helping sufferers, and provides leaflets and a counselling service. (address on p 175).

2 Being a carer

A carer is defined as anyone who spends time and energy looking after another person who needs extra attention. This could be a friend or neighbour but is most likely to be a close family member, such as a spouse or parent. How you first became a carer will be unique to you. Most people start in one of three ways: following a dramatic event such as a heart attack; or because they have willingly prepared themselves for a change in role to take care of a partner or relative after, for example, a heart operation; others find they have entered into a caring situation over time, without being aware of major changes, as the health of a person close to them slowly deteriorates.

What does it mean to be a carer?

Caring 'hours' can vary from a full-time activity if someone is seriously ill to as little as keeping a regular eye on their daily affairs. The aim of most carers is to help the person remain in their own home, leading a relatively independent life, for as long as possible. Wherever your position on the spectrum of care, it's likely that you are undertaking many of the jobs from the following list:

■ providing a safe and comfortable home;
■ doing practical jobs such as shopping, cooking, cleaning, laundry and gardening;

- giving personal care and basic nursing procedures;
- offering love, emotional support and company;
- providing help and advice on running personal affairs;
- reducing isolation and bringing a bit of the 'outside world' into the daily life of someone who can no longer get out and about.

Fact Box

Information published by the Carers National Association, for National Carers Week (June 1998)

- About 6.8 million people in the UK (one in seven adults) look after a relative or friend who cannot manage without help because of sickness, age or disability.
- About 4 million carers are women and 3 million are men.
- Estimates suggest that 51,000 carers are aged 18 years or under – most of them care for a parent.
- The state's financial support for carers is paltry – Invalid Care Allowance in 1997 was worth 11 per cent of national average earnings.
- Carers provide support worth £34 billion a year, yet many are excluded from state benefits.
- On average, 20,000 carers a year contact the CarersLine (see p 165).
- Some 65 per cent of carers report that their own health has suffered as a result of caring.

Source: General Household Survey 1995

Recognising yourself as a carer

Joan

'Peter had angina, a heart attack and a heart by-pass operation so I suppose I was a carer. I never thought of it like that.'

You may not think of yourself as a carer because you undertake your tasks out of love and friendship, and you may have fallen into the caring role because no one else is available. Many carers do not recognise themselves as such and therefore do not seek information or know how to look for further help. It is vital that you be aware that support and help are available and that you have choices and rights as a carer that go alongside the responsibilities. This chapter offers information, advice and support to anyone who cares in some way for a spouse, relative or friend. It cannot give you all of the answers or solve all of your problems but it may help you to understand better some of the issues around caring in general.

Your own needs as a carer

There are an estimated 6.8 million carers in the UK, over 1 million of whom provide substantial amounts of care. At times being a carer creates tremendous anxiety and distress: you may be undertaking tasks that feel difficult and unfamiliar, you are largely unpaid and untrained, and you are often on duty for 24 hours a day, seven days a week. Much will be expected of you, and this responsibility will tax your patience. In taking on an enduring commitment, you need to pace yourself, use a range of skills and experience, build up strong physical and mental systems, and maintain a good sense of humour. You won't always get it right – life is never completely straightforward and free from pressure – but there are many sources of support you can draw on to help things run smoothly. Chapters 6 and 7 tell you more about managing stress and finding ways to cope with very difficult situations.

Your perceptions and feelings as a carer

Penny, *a carers' support worker*

'Try to understand that feeling guilty, anxious and angry are usual emotions and reactions. They are often a sign that carers need to consider a period of respite. It's easy to say "don't worry", but try not to waste time doing so.'

You will have your ups and downs and there will be days when you feel you cannot cope. Even if you actively chose your caring situation, this will not stop you from having negative feelings, and although most people decide to care willingly, this will not be true of every carer. Professional people who work with carers understand that carers feel a range of very conflicting emotions and that sometimes they express these feelings towards their relative and towards the people who offer them support. Anger, frustration, fear, resentment and guilt often exist alongside other emotions such as sadness, love, anxiety and concern. Powerful emotions can drain and exhaust you, so try not to add 'worry' to the list. Worry and guilt are two emotions that cause much wasted energy. Look instead at problems from a positive angle – if you feel in control, you will cope well; if the problem is not within your control, spending time being worried or guilty won't improve the situation and may even prevent your finding a solution. It's often hard for carers to understand that they may have been bottling up a range of strong emotions but that it's absolutely OK to feel this way. Relieving the unhappy feelings is better than storing them up.

Sizing up the problem

It is still assumed in society today that a blood-tie or marriage relationship automatically makes a person (usually the woman in the partnership) the main carer and that in this role she must undertake a number of onerous, unpaid tasks. You may believe this yourself. It is often assumed by others that you have the ability to cope and that your capacity to care can stretch to meet all the demands that are placed on you. You may feel that other people expect so much from you – family members, GPs, social workers – and that you cannot let them down.

To help you come to terms with your role as a carer, it's important that you think about all of these expectations – including what you expect of yourself. If you feel confused or overwhelmed by the enormity of the task, talking to someone – perhaps another carer – might help. Look at the list below and tick off the feelings that have crossed your mind in recent weeks:

- lack of confidence and low feeling of self-worth;
- no credentials to do the job you are doing;
- worried about shortage of money;
- lack of recognition/status;
- not sure where to turn for allies or support;
- bewildered by the maze of services;
- unclear about what you can ask for;
- feel your own needs are always disregarded in favour of the 'patient';
- no time or space to be yourself.

These thoughts are very common, even if they have been only fleeting. Don't block them out. Accept that occasionally carers *do* feel unable to carry on and sometimes they are forced to take dramatic steps to make their voice heard. Support workers should do everything in their power to ease your position and avert a crisis. Unfortunately, not all carers have access to an adequate support system. If this applies to you, do speak to your GP or the duty social worker from the local authority's social services department and ask about additional help before crisis point is reached.

Setting boundaries

Janet, *a carers' support worker*

'People often become carers in a situation without being aware that carers do have choices.'

How did you become a carer? Did it creep up on you slowly over the years or happen suddenly because of a crisis? Whatever the original reason, at some point it is vital that you sit back and take stock of the current situation. Ask yourself a few searching questions and think logically and seriously about the answers. Talk to a counsellor (see Chapter 6) if an unbiased listener will help you sort out your feelings.

Ask yourself:

■ Why am I doing this job?
■ Am I being pressured by other people?
■ Will I feel that I have rejected someone I love if I stop?
■ Is the caring situation going to be long or short term?
■ Do I want to continue or to pass the responsibility over to others?
■ What are my options for change?

As a carer you must make a conscious decision about whether to continue with caring, because making a definite choice will help you to cope with the task, however difficult. There may be times when carers feel in despair, but when they perceive that they have no choice, that they were pressured into the situation by others or that they did not fully consider the seriousness of the situation they are more likely to become angry, resentful and suffer ill-health. There is nothing wrong with saying 'no' if you already feel over-burdened.

How 'good' is your caring situation?

Researchers studying informal caring, given by close relatives, have identified a model of a good caring situation that is recognised by professional people as an important factor in maintaining a positive and healthy life-style for the key people involved. Whilst acknowledging that no caring situation can hope to fulfil the ideal all of the time, it is important that everyone accepts the value of such a model and works towards achieving this as a goal.

The model list

- The carer makes a conscious choice whether or not to care.
- The carer is able to recognise their own limits and needs.
- The carer lives close by, but not in the same house.
- A network of care is set up, so that responsibility is shared.
- The carer has time to themselves and doesn't have to give up too much of their own life.
- The carer has access to information and help to learn skills.
- A good past relationship existed between the carer and the person being cared for.
- The dependent person wishes to stay as independent as possible.
- The dependent person retains their own friends.
- The carer fosters independence in the dependent person.
- Everybody keeps a sense of humour.
- Professional help is there when it is needed.
- The carer feels supported and valued.

What formal support is available for carers?

Increasingly the rights and needs of carers are being taken into account, although it has taken many years of lobbying by pressure groups and individual people and changes in legislation to reach the stage we are at now. The most relevant pieces of legislation are summarised below. Local authority documents such as a community care plan or charter may include information on help for carers and carers' rights. If you need a more detailed explanation of the rights and services to which you are entitled, contact your local social services department (social work department in Scotland), which will be listed in the telephone directory.

State provision

NHS and Community Care Act 1990

The NHS and Community Care Act brings together many pieces of legislation that date back to 1948 and is designed to help meet the care needs of older people and those with learning and physical disabilities and mental health problems, preferably in their own home or the area where they live. Social services take the lead role and work together with the NHS and voluntary organisations to offer a broad range of services for people in need and their carers. The services cannot promise to meet all needs, because community care is subject to certain eligibility criteria (see pp 37 and 42) but a trained person will assess the needs of the person you care for and then, if that person is eligible, arrange appropriate services in what is known as a 'care package'.

Carers (Recognition and Services) Act 1995

This Act came into force on 1 April 1996. It defines a carer as 'someone who provides (or intends to provide) a substantial amount of care on a regular basis', including children and young people under the age of 18 years. It contains two main elements that deal with the rights of carers: to ask for a separate assessment of their care needs when the person they care for is being assessed or reassessed; and the duty of the local authority to take into consideration the findings of this assessment when deciding which services to offer the person being cared for.

The Act requires social services departments, if requested to do so by a carer, to assess the ability of the carer to provide, or to continue to provide, care, and to take this into account when deciding what services to provide to the person being cared for. To qualify for an assessment a carer must be providing (or intending to provide) regular and substantial care, and the person they care for must be being assessed by social services at the same time. Because there is no official definition of 'regular' and 'substantial', each caring situation will be assessed individually. The assessment should recognise the carer's knowledge of the person, and the responsibility for the caring situation should be agreed as a shared undertaking between the carer and the social services department.

'The Carers' (Recognition and Services) Act 1995 has been one of the most significant developments in the history of the carers' movement. Not only did it recognise the rights of carers for the first time, but the campaign which led to the Carers Act showed the level of agreement there was about the rights and needs of carers.' Carers National Association

Local provision

Social services

Penny, *a carers' support worker*

'Information is often thrown at carers when they are desperate rather than when they can listen calmly – it's much better to "drip feed" small amounts when it is needed than for the carer to have to try to remember everything at once.'

Local social services departments are the main agencies for co-ordinating the provision of community care services. They may provide care direct, for example through their own home care service, or purchase care for your relative from voluntary or commercial organisations (sometimes called the independent sector). If you are new to caring, it may help to speak to a social worker to find out what services are available in your area and generally make yourself known, even if at this stage your needs are not great and you would not qualify for specific help.

Being informed

Janet, *a carers' support worker*

'Take a pen and paper with you when you visit the surgery or a professional person and make notes. GPs and social workers seem very busy to people who are frightened and anxious, but take your time.'

The time may come when your caring situation changes, and being informed is a major factor in maintaining control and dealing with difficult issues. Knowing what might be offered, even if you are a bit hazy, will make a basic starting point when you seek additional support. Don't try to remember everything you are told but do try to make a note of the key headings that services fall under; for example, your rights as a carer, domestic help, where you can obtain equipment. Set up an information folder and keep a notebook if it will help to organise your affairs.

Social services assessments, care plans and eligibility criteria

'When carers have an assessment, they get more services.' Carers National Association

Social services departments are responsible for providing a wide range of home, residential and day-care services. Unfortunately, demand for these services is heavy and most departments have limited financial resources so they apply strict eligibility criteria (tests) to decide which services to provide. These assessments, in some form, apply generally throughout the UK. Although the availability of individual services will differ from area to area, the example below is typical.

The first stage is an **assessment** that is intended to gather basic information about the situation and the care needs. At the end of the assessment an **agreement** is reached with the person (provided they are mentally capable) and their carer, defining exactly what the care needs are. For the purpose of assessment these fall into five basic categories:

- physical safety (eg the person has regular falls);
- physical disability (eg mobility, sight or hearing problems);
- mental health (eg dementia or severe depression leading to neglect);
- loss of independent living skills (eg unable to cook, wash or dress themselves);
- social needs (eg the person is very isolated and lonely).

The assessor then decides the **level of need** from **low** to **very high risk**:

1 Low immediate need.
2 Limited immediate need.
3 Some concerns.
4 Major concerns.
5 Major risk of harm.
6 Immediate/very high risk of harm.

Penny, *a carers' support worker*

'Unfortunately, there are gaps in services. Carers must ask for a proper assessment; don't give details over the telephone.'

To be eligible to receive any services from the local authority, a person must have needs at level 4 (major concern) or above in at least one of the six categories. If all the assessed needs fall at level 3 or below, the person is offered information and advice about sources of help. For example, details of voluntary and private organisations that provide a service similar to that of the local authority.

Once it is agreed that a person is eligible to receive services, discussions take place between everyone immediately involved to devise a care plan that best suits the needs of the family. A general package of services is offered that could include home care, meals-on-wheels, day care or residential care, etc. Before an individual service is agreed, it may be necessary to meet further eligibility criteria. For example, a person asking for residential care must have at least one set of needs at level 5 (major risk of harm) and agreement must also be reached about how much of each service a person is eligible to receive, such as one day per week at a day centre.

The eligibility criteria continue to apply if your relative is already receiving services. The needs of both of you will be **re-assessed** by means of a **review**, and services may change as a result of this process. Again, everyone immediately concerned will be fully involved and informed of any decisions about future care.

If you do not agree with the result of the assessment, you may appeal against it via the social services complaints procedure (a social worker can advise you about the process). Social services departments will investigate any complaint seriously and will suggest that you obtain independent advice. The local Citizens Advice Bureau may be able to advise you.

Charges

Social services departments can charge recipients of services (not carers) for many services they provide, depending on personal circumstances. Information outlining charging policies should be available from a customer relations department or similar office in the local authority; look for the telephone number under 'Social Services' ('Social Work' in Scotland) or ask at the Citizens Advice Bureau. After an assessment is completed, the costs of any care services offered will be explained before a care plan is agreed.

Charters

Most social services departments have drawn up charters that aim to tell people what they can expect from the agencies that provide community care services for adults. Two typical charters are summarised below; contact your social services office to enquire about local versions.

Community care charters complement the community care plan and are about the services that help people to remain in their own homes. They cover:

■ getting in touch;
■ understanding people's needs;
■ planning care;
■ the services people can expect to receive;
■ unmet needs;
■ information;
■ what to do if things go wrong;
■ relationships with people receiving services.

Charters for carers usually acknowledge the valuable role carers perform in caring for someone at home. They state that practical help for carers is a key priority for social services departments and set out how the department aims to respond to typical requests expressed by carers. The charters offer:

■ to share experiences;
■ recognition for carers;
■ practical help;
■ information and advice;
■ advice on welfare benefits;
■ a short break from caring.

Carers' support centres and workers

Janet, a carers' support worker

'Asking the questions that are right for you is important. Try not to judge what you think may be available – people are often surprised at the amount of services that exist. Use paper to jot down headings of things you want to discuss before you meet a professional person.'

There are many new schemes being set up around the country specifically to provide help and support for carers; they are run mainly by health and social services teams and voluntary organisations. The workers understand the problems and feelings of isolation experienced by carers and are specially trained to help carers receive relevant and up-to-date information, gain access to services and welfare benefits, and guide them in their caring role. Support workers welcome contact with you as a carer and will listen to your hopes, concerns and fears. Many produce newsletters, run local support groups for carers and have drop-in and respite care facilities.

Penny, a carers' support worker

'We understand that carers get to the end of their tether and may be quite close to physically harming their relative on occasion. Tension is usually relieved by shouting but sometimes carers can lose their temper more violently. If you feel it's time to look at ways of removing the strain, do seek help before you reach crisis point. If you feel in despair, give the Samaritans a call.'

Health care services

Decisions about what health services will be provided for people locally are taken by the health authority, who purchases these services from NHS trusts and the independent sector. You can get information about health services from your local community health council (see p 102). NHS and social services staff will work closely with your GP to maintain community care.

Local health services tend to fall into two categories:

■ **acute health care** – short-term care provided by NHS district hospital trusts that offer specialist tests and treatments through inpatient and outpatient services;

- **community health care** – provided by NHS community trusts that offer day-to-day care from a range of services, including district nursing, physiotherapy, occupational therapy and chiropody.

Eligibility criteria for NHS continuing health care

Many health authorities have developed a set of standards (eligibility criteria) to clarify who is entitled to receive long-term care in hospital. Typically, the decision to offer long-term care is based on an assessment of health needs and how often the person needs to see a consultant. If long-term, hospital-based care is not needed, social services and NHS professionals will prepare a package of care (set of services) to be provided at home or in a residential or nursing home.

The views and wishes of the person and their family are taken into account. If they do not agree with the decision to discharge the patient from hospital, they can ask an independent review panel to look at the decision. If this applies to you, the community health council (known as the health council in Scotland) (see p 102) can help you if you are unsure how to proceed.

For more *i*nformation

❶ Age Concern Factsheet 37 *Hospital discharge arrangements, and NHS continuing health care services.*

General practitioners (GPs)

The GP is the (family) doctor who has responsibility for day-to-day health care and sees patients at a surgery/health centre or, if necessary, in their home. A GP or an appropriate member of the surgery or health centre staff will give information, advice and support as well as treatment, and it is usually the doctor who refers your relative to other healthcare services. The health authority is responsible for the care provided by GPs.

Eric, *a GP*

'The surgery is often the first place to ask for help. Keep 'knocking on the door', as you sometimes need to get your GP to understand what you want. GPs should be a signpost to other services, and if you need a home visit make this clear.'

Pharmacists (chemists) and prescriptions

Pharmacists in local chemist shops provide a number of services to the community and are a valuable source of information about medicines, 'over-the-counter' treatments (which don't need a prescription) and any minor health problems that are not serious enough to take to a surgery. Pharmacists will advise you to speak to the GP if they feel there is a need for medical treatment. Before you speak to a pharmacist, make a list of all medication being taken by your relative so that he or she can be sure that drugs will not interact with each other.

In particular, a pharmacist is responsible for making up prescriptions for medicines or certain medical aids. You may take a prescription to any pharmacy but, for people living in rural areas, a dispensing service is available at surgeries and health centres if the nearest pharmacist/chemist shop is more than one mile away; ask about the availability of this service if you are unsure. There is normally a charge for prescriptions, but certain groups of people qualify for free medication:

■ people on Income Support;
■ people under 16 years of age;
■ people over 60;
■ people with certain illnesses;
■ women who are pregnant and for up to one year after the birth of the baby.

Pre-payment certificates are available to help spread the cost for people who need regular medication but do not qualify for free prescriptions. Enquire about these or any other pharmacy-related details at your local pharmacist/chemist shop or GP surgery.

Voluntary services

There is a wide range of voluntary organisations that provide services, self-help and support to carers at national and regional levels. Many of these organisations are directly contracted by the NHS and social services to provide care locally. No two areas will offer identical services, so you will have to find out what you can expect to obtain in your area. The two main sources of information about the voluntary sector can be found in the telephone directory under 'Council for Voluntary Services' (CVS) and 'Volunteer Bureaux' (or contact the National Association of Councils for Voluntary Service or the National Association of Volunteer Bureaux: addresses on p 172).

Some voluntary organisations only provide services that are broadly targeted, for example advice and information available from Citizens Advice Bureaux; others offer help related to specific conditions and illnesses. The latter are most likely to offer support through newsletters and self-help groups; some services provided by the voluntary sector carry charges to cover costs. In some places the voluntary sector provides a number of local facilities, professionally managed by well-trained staff, which are used on behalf of the community by NHS and social services; day centres and meals-on-wheels are good examples.

Making a complaint

If you are not happy with the services you receive from any organisation (NHS, social services, the private sector or voluntary agencies), try to resolve the situation as soon as possible by speaking to the person involved – this could be the senior nurse on duty, your care co-ordinator or a manager. If you are still not satisfied and wish to take the matter further, contact a customer relations department or equivalent (a voluntary organisation will have a management committee) and ask for details of their complaints procedure. For independent help with the complaints procedure, contact your local Citizens Advice Bureau or community health council (see pp 101 and 102).

Your own health needs

Don't forget to look after your own health and well-being. This may sound like a tall order but you do need to maintain your own strength:

- Eat regularly and properly – if you are preparing meals for someone else, try not to skimp on your own food.
- Take regular breaks from caring, even if you only find time to walk in the garden or read a book. Plan longer breaks at regular intervals.
- Arrange time away from the house to meet other people, because isolation can be a major problem for many carers. There are sitting services available that will send a volunteer to stay with your relative – try your local Age Concern group.
- Learn to move your relative safely, because strained and injured backs are a great problem for carers who are suddenly thrust into a caring role. Ask your district nurse or social worker about training courses or equipment.
- Take cat naps during the day if sleep at night is disturbed – without feeling guilty.
- Ask about help with housework or gardening if you are over-tired. Some local authorities and voluntary organisations run gardening schemes.

Emergency help

Carers often express fears about what to do if there is an accident and their relative falls. The advice from the ambulance service is: dial 999 for help. Do not attempt to move the person, as they will need to be assessed for injury.

First aid

If a situation occurs that needs prompt first aid, try to think and act calmly. You will be more effective and better able to reassure your relative.

If your relative falls, collapses or becomes seriously ill, either call an ambulance yourself or ask someone to do this for you. Then treat your relative according to their state of consciousness, until help arrives.

If conscious:

- reassure your relative that help is on the way;
- if your relative has difficulty breathing or complains of chest pains, gently raise them to a half-sitting position, with the head and shoulders supported;
- if your relative feels faint, sit them down, leaning forwards with head between the knees; encourage them to take deep breaths but not to over-breathe because this can quickly cause dizziness for other reasons;
- if your relative has fallen, do not move them unnecessarily as this may cause further injury;
- if your relative has diabetes, give them a sugary drink or a sugar lump or other sweet food;
- do **not** give anything to eat or drink if your relative does not have diabetes.

If unconscious:

- if possible, lie your relative on the floor on their side; otherwise try to position the head with the jaw forwards in order to maintain a clear airway and to prevent saliva and the tongue falling backwards;
- remove dentures;
- loosen tight clothing;
- cover your relative with a blanket to keep warm;
- do **not** give any food or fluids of any kind.

If you become ill or need extra help

If you become ill and need additional help during the day, you can contact the duty social services officer or your GP. For assistance outside office hours, contact the social services emergency duty team or a medical answering service. (Look up the numbers in the telephone directory and put them by the telephone now.)

Emergency help systems

Many local authorities and some charities operate an emergency call system that is linked via the telephone service to specially trained operators. (It may not be available to everyone.) A charge is usually made to help fund the system, which will vary from area to area. If no such facility exists in your area, contact the organisations below for details of their national service.

- **Age Concern** and **AidCall** have joined forces to help people to remain independent by providing a 24-hour emergency response service. A free demonstration is available. Charging options offer annual or quarterly payment that includes installation, monitoring and maintenance. (Address on p 163.)
- **SeniorLink** run by **Help the Aged** operates as a national community alarm telephone system for older people who do not qualify for a locally run system or cannot afford the fee. SeniorLink is open to women aged over 60 and men over 65. There is a weekly fee of £1.00. (Address on p 169.)

Carer's emergency card

You might be concerned that you could have an accident or be taken ill while you are away from home, leaving the person you care for alone. You can obtain an emergency identity card that gives information about you as a carer so that your relative will not be left unattended. Cards are available from the Carers National Association (address on p 165).

Carers' advice line

A telephone help-line offering a wide range of information to carers operates nationally for the cost of a local call. Run by the Carers National Association, its slogan is: *Whatever your caring responsibility, whatever your question, call* **CarersLine** *on 0345 573 369.* Lines are open Monday to Friday, 10 am–noon and 2–4 pm.

For more *i*nformation

i Research Institute for Consumer Affairs (address on p 173) for information about emergency help systems and services.

Fact Box

■ 70 per cent of carers do so for over 100 hours per week.
■ The average time spent caring is 11 years.
■ 28 per cent of carers are aged 50–59, 1 in 20 is aged over 80.
■ 48 per cent of carers look after a spouse.
■ 53 per cent of carers had not been informed of their rights even though their relative had been assessed.
■ 38 per cent did not know they were entitled to an assessment.
■ 55 per cent had their services increased following an assessment.
■ 59 per cent were happy with the outcomes of the assessment.

Source: a UK survey *Still Battling?*, published by Carers National Association, June 1997

Conclusion

This chapter has offered material to help you focus on your role as a carer and given you an insight into the nature of caring. Reading the information may have been painful for you, especially if it raised uncomfortable questions that you found difficult to answer. Hopefully, if you are one of the many carers who are unfamiliar with the official system, it will encourage you to seek support and ask for an assessment of your caring situation. The statistics in the Fact Box give you a clear indication that you are not alone in the caring business. Take comfort in the fact that the predicament of carers is now under open discussion and their efforts are being increasingly recognised and supported.

For more information

i Age Concern Factsheet 6 *Finding help at home*.

i Carers National Association provides support, information and advice (address on p 165).

i Counsel and Care offers free counselling, information and advice for older people and carers, including specialist advice about using independent agencies and the administration of trust funds for single payments (eg respite care) (address on p 166).

i *Coping with Caring* leaflet from pharmacies/chemist shops.

i Information Line – a free, national information service by Age Concern for senior citizens, their relatives, carers and friends. (0800 00 99 66)

i Help the Aged provides a range of services, including information leaflets and helplines (eg 'Winter Warmth' for information about keeping warm during cold weather) (address on p 169).

i *Making the Most of Being a Carer* by Ann Whitfield (Need 2 Know Series), published by Forward Press. Available from bookshops.

3 Daily living

The risk factors for coronary heart disease were outlined in Chapter 1. Although gender and family history are fixed, many others can be lessened by making changes in lifestyle, and this chapter discusses how this may be done. Changes include:

- improving the diet, to lower blood cholesterol levels and reduce obesity;

- taking more exercise, to keep the heart muscle fit;

- giving up smoking, to reduce by half the chances of having a heart attack;

- lowering high blood pressure, to reduce strain on the heart – especially if blood vessels are already clogged with fatty deposits;

- managing stress – Chapters 6 and 7 offer help with reducing anxiety levels.

Many people are concerned about the effect of a heart condition on sexual relationships and are unsure how to ask professional people for advice. This chapter gives some answers, and if you or your relative are still uncertain you can use the information to help ask a few personal questions. Not all of the changes will apply to the person you care for but the information could be useful for other family *members, especially if an increased risk of heart problems runs in the family. The thought of making major life-style changes on top of everything else that has happened may be daunting, so the chapter starts by offering some tips about making changes in general.*

Sylvia

'I was relieved when the doctor told us that there were lots of things we could do to help prevent another heart attack. It's easier to cope if you think you are helping.'

Celia, an occupational therapist

'The value of rehabilitation must not be under-estimated, as the majority of heart attacks are survived.'

Any heart condition is serious; if you were with your relative at the time of a heart attack, you are probably afraid that it might happen again. Most people feel anxious during the convalescent stage and need reassurance that ordinary life can resume. Lots of support will be available in the early days to help you both begin the process of getting back to normal. Looking after someone who is ill brings responsibilities, and you will want to do your best for your relative in every possible way. Follow the advice given by professional people and you and your relative will soon slip into a new pattern of life.

Fact Box

Here are a few positive facts to help your relative overcome any anxieties:

- Most people make an excellent recovery after a heart attack.
- Most people are fitter after they have introduced changes to their life-style – improved diet, increased exercise and relaxation.

- The heart, like any other part of the body, is designed to repair itself and can compensate for some damage that is not life-threatening.
- After heart surgery or a heart attack, it is normal to tire more easily and this is not necessarily a sign that things are going wrong.
- Self-help is a great boost to recovery.

Elsie and Tom

'After the heart attack, the occupational therapist told us to stop, take stock and think carefully about how we were running our lives and what our hectic life-style was doing to our bodies.'

Making changes

A change in circumstances is always triggered by some event, however minor. If you think about major changes in the past, something happened that set you off on a new course of action. Sometimes the event is not within your control and you feel unsettled until you have come to terms with the new situation. The process is easier to deal with if you allow time to work your way naturally through a series of stages.

The first period is often called the *unfreezing* stage. It's the time to let everything settle down and accept that you can't put the clock back. It's important that you both spend time talking about how your relative's illness has changed your lives: don't try to block out any feelings, because you won't be able to plan for the future while you still feel upset about what has happened. Allow yourself to grieve about the past; it's perfectly normal to want to do this when a traumatic event has taken place. Let relatives and friends offer support.

The next stage is called *moving forward*. It's the time to start making changes. Your relative will be on the road to recovery and you will both feel ready to plan for the future. Don't rush this stage, and talk to other people if you feel anxious about making decisions. Your plans might cover a range of issues – financial, health and practical matters. They all need careful thought.

When you and your relative have made decisions and begun to sort out the practical issues, you are entering stage three; this time is called the *re-freezing* period. It becomes *solid* when you both feel comfortable about the changes that have taken place. This final stage won't happen swiftly, so don't be alarmed or feel there is something wrong if it takes a while before life feels close to normal again. Be honest with yourselves about accepting the changes, because pretending and putting on a brave face when you feel anxious inside can be stressful. Better times will return eventually.

> ## *Sylvia*
>
> 'I will always remember the occupational therapist saying to me "Understanding makes coping easier".'

If you or your relative are having difficulty accepting that change is taking place, it might help to talk about what is holding you up. Sometimes problems are perceived to be greater than they really are. It often happens that, as soon as you think you have dealt with a 'worry', it springs up again in another guise. This may be because you haven't truly come to terms with the problem, so it continues to dominate your thoughts. The change process is a slow business, so don't rush into a false sense of acceptance. As you resolve problems, bit by bit, the nightmare of dealing with a huge change will feel less of a burden. Follow these guidelines for the future:

- Do look forward.
- Do make a list of the good things in life – however trivial.
- Do talk to someone about difficult decisions.
- Do accept that life moves forward.
- Don't rush yourselves.
- Don't bottle up feelings.

- ■ Don't feel guilty.
- ■ Don't try to place blame.
- ■ Don't look over your shoulder, hankering for a 'better' past.

Diet

Sylvia

'I've learned to look after myself, too. It's important that I keep going, so I try to get enough sleep and to eat properly.'

Rita, *a dietitian*

'"Variety is the spice of life". This is particularly true in terms of diet – taking a wide variety of food can ensure health needs are met.'

Diet is an important factor in any programme designed to reduce the risk of coronary heart disease. A review of what your relative eats will be high on the list of changes that you will need to help them make. Dietary advice is readily available for patients after heart surgery or a heart attack. Talk to the practice nurse, who will have a selection of leaflets, and ask the GP if your relative can be referred to a dietitian for specific advice tailored to their needs. The following information outlines the links between food and heart disease.

Obesity (very overweight)

Excess weight causes a great strain on the whole body, especially the heart and joints. Overweight people are more likely to have raised blood pressure and an increased risk of developing diabetes as well as heart and circulatory (cardiovascular) diseases. Many heart problems – angina attacks, high levels of cholesterol and high blood pressure – improve considerably when extra weight is shed. Some people even reduce their need for medication.

Rita, *a dietitian*

'Watch your weight! Don't let it creep up – it's much harder to take off than put on.'

Over the years, slimming has become a fashionable, money-making business with a number of unsuitable 'crash' diets being promoted by their manufactures and ill-informed press articles. Unfortunately, miracle diets don't work for more than a short time and many are unsafe. They rely heavily on starving the body of food rather than encouraging dieters to change their poor eating habits through a balanced and sensible eating plan. The only effective way to lose weight permanently is to eat the amount required by the body to balance its daily energy needs – too much and our bodies store the excess calories as fat for use in future emergencies.

Some people inherit a tendency to be a certain shape and gain weight more readily than others. Nevertheless, anyone who eats fewer calories than they burn up will lose weight, especially if they link their healthy diet to getting sufficient exercise. When trying to cut back on calories, it's important not to lose valuable vitamins and minerals in the process. In everyday terms this means selecting foods that give a high nutritional value per calorie. When shopping or eating out choose:

- more fruit and vegetables to increase the fibre, vitamins and minerals;
- more starchy foods (bread, rice, pasta), because they fill you up and contain no more calories than protein;
- wholemeal versions rather than white or processed foods, because they contain more fibre, vitamins and minerals;
- less fatty foods, because fat is twice as high in calories as the same weight of starch or protein;
- less sugary foods such as sweet drinks, cakes and biscuits, because these foods contain high-energy calories but no true food value; you can cut down on sugar without losing any nourishment;
- less salt, because too much salt can lead to high blood pressure, thus increasing the risk of strokes and heart disease;

■ less alcohol, because this has a higher calorie content than starch or protein.

A lot of benefit can be gained by making minor changes. It's important to continue to enjoy food, so don't make dramatic changes over-night. Introduce new foods and cooking methods gradually and buy a variety of foods so that a nutritious balance is maintained.

Rita, *a dietitian*

'Keep your interest in food – it's never too late to try new foods, new tastes and new styles of cooking.'

Blood cholesterol levels

The risk of coronary heart disease is directly linked to levels of cholesterol in the blood. The higher the level of total cholesterol, the higher the risk. Too much cholesterol in the blood causes a build-up of deposits on artery walls. The cholesterol circulating in the blood stream comes from two sources: it is produced by your body and it is absorbed from foods that naturally contain the substance. Some people inherit a tendency towards high levels of blood cholesterol. If this is a family problem, it would be wise for younger family members to seek advice from a doctor and have a blood cholesterol test.

Cholesterol is an oily substance that plays an important part in the make-up and work of body cells. Most cholesterol found in the blood is produced by the liver, and is carried to tissues in the body by substances, called lipoproteins, in the blood stream. The main sources of foods naturally rich in cholesterol are eggs, liver, kidneys and some shellfish. However, don't rush to cut out these foods, because scientists have shown that cutting back on foods that are high in natural cholesterol is not the best way to reduce blood cholesterol levels.

The most important point to understand when reviewing diet is the overall *amount and type* of fat eaten rather than the actual cholesterol itself. Some fats are essential for good health and others are harmful. Foods high in *saturated* fats increase blood cholesterol levels, whereas foods high in *polyunsaturated* and *monounsaturated* fats can help to reduce it. Don't worry about trying to understand the scientific words for different types of fat; if you follow the guidelines below it will be easy to cut back on harmful fats and to eat those that help reduce cholesterol levels.

Saturated fats are found mainly in the following foods, and tend to be solid in consistency:

- meat (including meat products) – beef, lamb, pork, suet, lard and dripping;
- dairy products: milk, butter, cream and cheese;
- some vegetable oils and hard margarines containing coconut and palm oils that have been specially treated to make them solid.

Unsaturated fats are found in the following foods and oils, and tend to be soft or liquid in consistency:

- vegetable oils: sunflower, corn, soya, rape seed and olive;
- soft margarines: all labelled 'high in polyunsaturated fat';
- certain foods: nuts, oily fish such as tuna, mackerel, sardines, salmon and trout.

If you are unsure about the type of fat a product contains, check the label – all foods carry a description of the contents. Manufacturers are keen to promote healthy foods so the word 'polyunsaturated' will be prominent on the packaging. Reducing the overall amount of fat that is consumed is the main goal, because this will help lower weight as well as cholesterol levels.

Tips to reduce fat

- Use skimmed or semi-skimmed milk rather than full-cream milk.
- Trim off all the visible fat from meat and choose as lean a cut as you can afford.

- Minced meats always have a higher fat content than large cuts.
- Cut down on the amount of meat products you buy, especially sausages, salami and meat pies, because their fat content is very high.
- Change to low-fat versions of dairy products; cottage and Dutch cheeses are good, and look for the word 'polyunsaturates' when you choose soft margarines and spreads.
- Eat more fish and poultry of any variety.
- Remove the skin from poultry.
- Drain away all excess fat during the cooking process.
- If you frequently use a deep fat fryer or pan, gradually change over to other methods that exclude fat rather than using extra: grilling meats and poaching or microwaving fish in a little milk with lots of pepper are easy ways to start.
- Cut out completely fatty snacks such as crisps and biscuits – bring in fruit and yoghurt for puddings or eating between meals.

Rita, *a dietitian*

'Eat regularly – start the day well with breakfast but remember "healthy eating" guidelines and *lose* the frying pan.'

Salt (sodium chloride)

There has been pressure from dietitians in the past to cut down on the amount of salt in the diet because too much contributes to high blood pressure, increasing the risk of heart and kidney disease and strokes. Most people eat far more salt than their body requires, some up to ten times as much as they need. About half comes from processed foods (tinned foods, pies, cooked meats), about one-quarter is added at the cooking stage and at the table and the remainder is naturally present in foods. Salt intake can be reduced in lots of ways and very soon taste buds will adjust to the change; aim to reduce total consumption to a maximum of one teaspoonful per day, not forgetting the hidden salt in tinned foods.

It is difficult to calculate the amount of salt in canned food because it may be present in different forms – for example, brine, monosodium glutamate and soy sauce are used to enhance flavour. The best advice is to use processed food sparingly because you have less control over the salt content than foods prepared at home. A study at Duke University in the USA found that the added salt content of processed foods can be reduced significantly by rinsing them under running water. Green beans rinsed for one minute lost 41 per cent of their sodium content, and tuna fish lost even more. The salt content of most condiments and seasonings is also high. For example, one teaspoon of table salt contains about 1,965 mg of sodium chloride compared with 1,716 mg in one tablespoon of soy sauce.

Tips to reduce salt

■ Gradually reduce the amount added to food during cooking and increase other flavours such as herbs, spices and lemon juice to change and highlight flavours.

■ Reduce the number of snack foods that are obviously coated in salt (eg crisps and salted nuts); this will also cut down on fat intake, so is a double bonus.

■ Try hard not to add salt at the table: taste first and add salt sparingly if necessary but preferably try something else – lemon juice and black pepper both enhance taste.

■ Cut salted, processed foods (eg meat pies, bacon, gammon, tinned foods in brine) completely out of the diet if possible – there are lots of fresh alternatives.

■ Look at the packaging and buy foods that are labelled 'no added salt'; many food producers are aware of the health risks and 'healthy' products are readily available.

Rita, *a dietitian*

'Fluids are important; don't restrict them unless your doctor says so. Aim for eight cups per day, including water, fruit juice and hot drinks.'

Alcohol

Small amounts of alcohol (one or two drinks per day) may be beneficial in reducing the risks of heart disease. Heavy drinking, however, raises blood pressure and increases risks. Alcohol 'bingeing' – drinking large amounts in one bout – is also not good for the system, because the liver must work very hard to clear the toxic substances from the body. The best policy is to keep within the recommended limits of 14 units per week for women and 21 units per week for men. A 'unit' or standard drink is equivalent to a pub measure:

beer	½ pint
wine	1 standard glass
spirits	1 standard measure

One group of scientists has suggested that small quantities of alcohol could be good for people with heart problems because it helps the arteries to dilate, enabling the blood to flow more freely. This thinking has led many health writers and doctors to promote moderate alcohol consumption as desirable. However, it is important to look at the other side of the story, which shows a different picture. Another group of scientists researching the causes of high blood pressure have found a close link between alcohol and hypertension. The results of their studies seem to show that the more alcohol people drank, the greater their risk of high blood pressure. This information contradicted previous thinking, and therefore needed some explanation, because the obvious conclusion should have been that if alcohol dilates blood vessels then blood pressure ought to fall, not increase. Further evidence has indicated that the raised blood pressure was caused by the direct effect of alcohol on the heart muscle. The people who took part in this study, and who drank in moderation, were shown to have enlarged hearts and high blood pressure.

In the face of all the evidence from many studies throughout the world, the strongest message for everyone is that alcohol should be drunk in moderation. It is still strongly linked to many other causes of illness and death – liver disease, stroke, cancer and accidental death – and there is no firm evidence that it prevents heart disease. Everyone (even people who do not have a heart problem) is advised to restrict their drinking by having at least two or three alcohol-free days each week to give their bodies a rest.

For people with existing heart problems the advice is more definite: ask your doctor for guidelines about drinking, because circumstances vary with the individual. Alcohol may make the situation worse rather than better for anyone who suffers from heart problems. However, with the doctor's permission alcohol need not be banned completely; the indications are that drinking *small, well-controlled* amounts will do no lasting harm. Have an occasional glass of wine but stay well below the recommended levels for people without heart problems, and avoid situations where a large, rich meal is accompanied by several drinks and over-excitement. This combination of events is more likely to put pressure on an over-stressed heart. You can encourage your relative to enjoy the party but stay in control. For people who experience difficulties in cutting back on alcohol, local and national organisations offer self-help groups and counselling to help gain control of the problem: look in the telephone directory, ask at the Citizens Advice Bureau or contact Drinkline (address on p 168).

Tips to reduce alcohol

For your relative:

- Set a reasonable limit (get medical advice about drinking levels), and don't be persuaded to binge.
- Be firm about saying 'no' when drinking with friends – explain why but don't feel that an apology is necessary.
- To cut down on drinking, sip drinks slowly, miss out rounds and choose alcohol-free drinks to quench thirst.

For you:

- If your relative was a regular heavy drinker either at the pub or at home, encourage them to change their habits; if they are bored or stressed don't use alcohol to blur the issues.
- If your relative needs to drink less alcohol but is finding it difficult to cut back, remind them of the long-term benefits/risks; ask family and friends for support and talk to a counsellor yourself if the going is really tough.

For both of you:

- When pouring out drinks at home, be very aware of the size of the glass – home measures tend to be more generous than pub measures and many people under-estimate the strength of some beers and lagers.
- Think about ways of having a treat with the money that is being saved – little rewards are good for the morale.

Smoking

Celia, *an occupational therapist*

'Smoking – quit for life, *your* life.'

Tobacco is the substance most linked to the cause of coronary heart disease. It is a myth that smoking may not be harmful. The evidence from a large number of scientific studies shows that all forms of smoking damage health: cigarettes, cigars and pipes. (Lifelong pipe smokers don't inhale, so the tar is deposited around the mouth, which is where they get cancer; people who previously smoked cigarettes and change to a pipe tend to continue to inhale, so their risk of lung cancer remains to which they add risk in the mouth.) A person who smokes cigarettes greatly increases their risk of high blood pressure and is twice as likely as a non-smoker to have a heart attack. It's never too late to feel the benefits of giving up, and it's the most effective change that anyone who suffers from a heart problem can make to improve their health.

Tobacco smoke contains many poisonous chemicals that play a significant part in the build-up of atherosclerosis, the process that 'hardens' and 'furs up' the artery walls. Moreover, chemical action makes the blood thicker, increasing the chance of blood clots. The most serious damage is caused by three main substances:

- **Carbon monoxide**   This takes the place of some of the oxygen in the blood stream, so vital organs are deprived of essential oxygen. Carbon monoxide also aggravates arterial disease, contributing to high blood pressure.
- **Tar**   This lines the tissues of the lungs, reducing the amount of oxygen getting across to the blood stream. Tar also causes irritation and inflammation of the lungs, leading to the development of chronic bronchitis and emphysema, two conditions that can eventually contribute to heart failure. (And, of course, there is the risk of developing lung cancer.)
- **Nicotine**   This is an addictive substance that acts as a mental depressant but its chief danger is its ability to act swiftly on artery walls, causing them to contract very strongly. These muscle spasms vastly reduce the flow of blood to the heart muscle and are the major cause of angina.

Most people understand and accept that smoking is bad for their health, especially people with heart disease. If the person you are caring for has been in hospital, they will have been told of the dangers and may already have given up. This is not an easy thing to do, because long-term smokers are usually addicted to the nicotine and will suffer withdrawal symptoms. Stopping smoking can be difficult during convalescence when factors such as boredom, fear of recurrent illness and anxiety about the future increase levels of stress. Be ready to offer encouragement, as you can help in lots of ways.

Tips to stop smoking

- Listen to your relative and try not to criticise any lapses – be sympathetic but firm.
- Don't suggest that your relative start smoking again – however irritable they become!

- Talk to other ex-smokers or telephone the freephone helpline run by the independent charity Quitline (0800 002 200) that provides confidential and practical advice for people wanting to give up smoking.
- Change routines so that old habits don't make it easy to light up – suggest that your relative sits in a different chair, drinks tea instead of coffee and does something different after a meal – all times when a cigarette might have been smoked. Identify danger times/places and alter behaviour if necessary.
- Offer plenty of fruit and fruit juice, because ex-smokers need to flush the chemicals well out of their system – the vitamin C helps rid the body of nicotine. Be careful, though, not to increase calorie intake with foods that have a high sugar content.
- Suggest different forms of entertainment to help cope with the boredom, particularly things that use the hands.
- Chat about the money that is being saved and think of ways to treat yourselves.
- Offer plenty of praise and support but don't overdo the sympathy – some sensitive people would rather not be reminded. Ask which approach works best.
- Suggest that your relative tells family and friends; that way they will know not to smoke in your relative's presence and, hopefully, won't tease about trying to give up.

Exercise

> **Celia, an occupational therapist**
>
> 'Add years to your life by adding life to your years – participate in exercise you enjoy.'

Exercise is good news for everyone, even for people who have heart problems. The heart is a muscle and, like all muscles, its action can be strengthened by exercise and its blood supply increased. A heart 'trained' by exercise pumps more blood with each beat, so it doesn't have to beat so fast to move the same amount of blood. In the past, treatment for people who suffered heart attacks meant long periods of inactivity and bed rest to allow the heart to heal. This is no longer thought to be necessary: patients are now encouraged to get out of bed and move around very soon after the attack, and are usually offered a rehabilitation programme before discharge.

Information in a book can only be written in a general way, so before taking any form of exercise, all people with a heart problem *must* check with their doctor first and be sure they understand the type and level of exercise that is suitable for them. As a carer you can help your relative to plan their exercise sensibly, perhaps with the advice of a physiotherapist who is skilled at helping people get the best from an exercise programme. You could join in – shared exercise is much more pleasurable than slogging it out alone.

Why is exercise good for us?

It is never too late to derive some benefit from exercise, and the advantages are well proven. Exercise helps lower blood pressure and improves physical strength, mobility and mental well-being. Physical activity protects the body by maintaining smooth movement in the joints, by strengthening bones and by increasing the efficiency of the heart muscle. It can help to prevent osteoporosis and further heart problems. The Health Education Authority, a government-funded organisation (see p 169), recommends daily exercise that is energetic enough to make you feel puffed; this level is more than 'merely being busy'. Nevertheless, lighter, less frequent exercise is also beneficial.

It's good to assess the exercise benefits of everything your relative does so that daily activities such as gardening, housework, climbing the stairs and walking to the shops are included in their overall fitness plan. Encourage them to put a bit of vigour into daily living and plan extra activities at least three times a week. Exercise is very good for reducing stress, because it boosts the hormones that produce feelings of happiness and the movement gently relaxes muscle tension.

The message from the experts promotes the three **S**s – stamina, strength and suppleness – as the key elements in keeping fit.

- **Stamina** increases the ability to keep going without getting breathless or suffering from aching muscles.
- **Strength** helps the body to put extra effort into pushing, pulling and lifting safely and without too much difficulty.
- **Suppleness** allows your body to bend, twist and stretch without strain and discomfort.

Ring the changes to prevent boredom

John

'I wish someone had encouraged me to exercise earlier – I thought it was for fitness freaks but cycling has made me feel great.'

When planning an exercise programme choose a range of activities that really get the body moving; variety means you and your relative can choose according to mood and the weather without becoming bored. Exercise should be pleasant and fun, not stressful and competitive. Set achievable aims because, if the effort feels too great, you may both lose enthusiasm. All exercise is safer if muscles are given time to warm up and cool down before and after the main exertion; athletes spend time doing special actions that stretch muscles and increase the heart rate. It's not necessary to learn specific warm up and cool down routines for any of the leisure activities listed below but 'start and finish slowly' is a simple rule that can be applied to all basic types of exercise. The following activities will help you and your relative become fitter without being too strenuous and are all classed as leisure hobbies rather than exercises for fitness fanatics; some can be done alone, some need a partner. If you would like to join a club, look in the Yellow Pages or ask for details at the local library.

Walking is a good choice if you have both been inactive recently, because it boosts stamina and allows fitness to build up at a steady rate. It can be done anywhere, needs no special equipment and is free, relaxing and pleasurable if shared with a companion. A beginner should aim to walk one mile in 20–30 minutes, increasing the pace and distance over a few weeks. For sensible preparation and finish, start walking at a slow pace and increase speed and exertion until you are walking briskly; gradually slow down as you approach the end of the walk, and when you reach home give your muscles a gentle stretch before you sit down.

Swimming is a good exercise for people of all ages, because it combines stamina, strength and suppleness. It is often described as the ideal activity, and it's a great stress reducer – and especially good for people who are overweight or have joint or back problems, because the water supports the body. Many people live within reasonable distance of a swimming pool and the charges are often reduced for certain groups of people.

Cycling is another good exercise to improve on the three Ss. It's recommended for people who are overweight and helps reduce stress as well as being particularly pleasurable. Cycling in the fresh air is the best choice but an indoor cycle machine provides an alternative way to get pedalling (you can pedal while reading a book or watching TV!).

Golf helps build up stamina and strength, provides fresh air and an opportunity to make new friends. If you have never played golf before, you will be pleasantly surprised at how energising it can be. Enjoy the scenery and don't overdo the sustenance offered at the nineteenth hole!

Bowling is low on stamina and strength but excellent for suppleness and relaxation. Join a club to get the best advantage from indoor and grass bowls, and try the ten pin variety for some challenging fun.

Badminton is a fun game that suits all ages as long as you are matched with someone of similar ability. Join a club to get some tuition and don't be too competitive. Build up skills at a pace that is comfortable. It's quite a vigorous sport that can be played at a range of speeds from gentle to fast and furious, so your relative should check with the doctor before starting this type of exercise.

67

Exercise and dance classes are readily available in most areas. Ask at a leisure centre about classes to suit your relative's age and ability level. Both types of activity are good for stamina, strength and suppleness, and dancing is especially relaxing and enjoyable.

Yoga is an excellent form of exercise to control movements and breathing and to encourage muscle relaxation. It's good for suppleness and strengthens body muscles but there is not much benefit for stamina, so if your relative gets hooked on yoga combine it with another exercise that helps to strengthen the heart muscle as well.

Exercising safely

Exercise takes many forms so be sure to choose activities that give the best physical results combined with lots of pleasure. No one will suggest that your relative takes up exhausting forms of exercise such as hard jogging or squash. Before starting any form of exercise, it is vital that they get permission from their doctor, and are aware of a few safely rules.

- Start the regimen gradually and build up the exertion at a rate that feels comfortable; this is not training for the Olympics!
- Don't exercise for at least two hours after a meal, because the digestive system places an automatic demand on the blood supply to digest the food.
- Wear clothing that is loose and comfortable, and shoes or trainers that provide adequate support.
- Muscles need to warm up and cool down before and after exercise, so never rush straight into the most strenuous part of the activity; start and stop at a gentle pace.
- Drink plenty of fluids, but not alcohol because this increases dehydration.
- Stop immediately if there are any signs of breathlessness, chest pains or feeling unwell in any way. If exercise has caused problems, however minor, inform the doctor before continuing with the programme.

For more *i*nformation

i The Sports Council provides general information about all sports (address on p 174).

Leg cramps

Even mild increases in exercise may cause leg cramps for people who have peripheral vascular disease, a condition in which the blood supply to the legs is restricted because of 'hardening' and 'furring up' of the arteries. The extra oxygen needed by the muscles cannot be supplied and causes sharp pains, particularly in the calf muscles, that cease as soon as the person takes a rest. In severe cases the pains are brought on after walking only short distances on flat ground. Your relative's doctor will advise about taking exercise if leg cramps are painful.

Sleeping well

Tension and stress are common causes of sleep problems, causing early waking or difficulty dropping off when thoughts race around the brain. If stress is making you or your relative sleep badly, don't rush for medication. Instead, try practising the relaxation techniques described in Chapter 6. And be aware that many older people naturally take longer to fall asleep, are more likely to wake during the night and tend to wake earlier in the morning. However, early waking is also a symptom of depression, which may benefit from treatment.

Tips to help settle at night

- Go to bed at a regular time, with a regular routine.
- Make everything as cosy as possible – warm room and comfortable bed.
- Don't eat a big meal late in the day.
- Avoid drinks that contain alcohol or caffeine later in the day, and choose a milky drink at bedtime.

■ Cut back on evening fluids if a full bladder is the cause of waking.

■ Read or listen to the radio until you naturally feel sleepy. If you wake in the night, do the same or get up and watch some television and repeat the milky drink with a biscuit if you are feeling hungry – don't lie tossing and turning.

■ Take regular exercise, but don't be too strenuous late in the day as this type of exercise releases hormones that are stimulating.

Sexual relationships

When to resume sexual relationships after a heart attack or surgery or how great the risks are for someone who has angina are questions that many people avoid asking because of embarrassment. Your relative's doctor will be able to reassure them about their condition and will not be embarrassed to discuss the matter. Generally, the advice to people with heart conditions is to treat sex like any other type of exercise. Regular sexual activity that induces slight breathlessness is good news: it aids recovery by strengthening the heart muscle, relieves stress and adds to the feeling of well-being. Normal sex with a known partner puts a strain on the heart equivalent to climbing two flights of stairs! Information and advice are available from SPOD, the Association to Aid Sexual and Personal Relationships of People with a Disability (address on p 174).

In the rare cases where sexual activity has brought on a heart attack there are usually other factors that contributed to the situation. A heavy meal or too much alcohol, and the excitement of having sex with a new partner or unknown person can all put additional strain on the heart. Like any other form of exercise, it's wise to take note of how the body feels: if sexual activity causes discomfort or chest pains, stop immediately and talk to the doctor about the problem.

Impotence

Peripheral vascular disease (see p 9), the condition that causes painful cramps while walking, can also affect sexual performance in some men, leading to difficulty achieving or maintaining an erection. Poor blood supply to the penis may be a factor, but other causes – stress, tiredness, side effects from drugs and leaking veins that cannot retain blood in the penis – all affect the quality of an erection. If impotence is a problem for your relative, do encourage him to seek help from a doctor because a range of special treatments are available. One question that will be asked is whether there is a morning erection, as this information will help the doctor to decide whether there are physical causes. A change in drug treatment or some relaxation therapy may be all that is needed to improve the situation.

Signs of depression

Immediately after an illness or operation, the time is filled with rest and treatment. However, as your relative recovers, the problem of boredom may become apparent. It's well worth giving this period some thought because, although having time to think about the past and the future will help in adjusting to the change, it is important not to let a state of depression develop, brought on by apathy or feelings of uselessness. Some signs of minor depression – for example, weeping and being withdrawn – are common after a serious illness, but, if you feel that these signs are getting worse, do encourage your relative to seek help from the doctor before it becomes difficult to manage. Talking and listening are excellent ways of starting self-help treatment.

Relieving boredom

Elsie

'Tom was fine at first but I kept finding him staring into space. My daughter helped by suggesting we joined a club together.'

There are many ways to lift the spirit and relieve the boredom. Talk to your relative about the kinds of activity and company they would or would not enjoy. Get out of the house as soon as it is practicable to have a change of scene and overcome early fears about leaving a safe place. Enlist the help of family and friends for all manner of support – from shoppers and drivers to companions and listeners – but try to be aware of how your relative feels, because you may need to act as gatekeeper if too many people want to help.

The public library is the best source of information: most branches carry a wide range of details about local services, with some specialist facilities targeted at carers. As well as books of all sorts, look out for:

- lists of clubs and hobby groups;
- audio and video tapes;
- mobile and doorstep library services for home delivery of books and tapes to people who have difficulty getting to a library because of illness, disability or caring responsibilities;
- 'Talking News' style services providing a range of interesting items via postal tapes – usually for visually impaired people but often extended to people with other disabilities;
- 'befrienders' schemes where volunteers come to the house to chat or play games with people who are temporarily or permanently housebound;
- branches of University of the Third Age (U3A) that offer a vast range of day-time study and recreational classes for older people who wish to keep their minds stimulated (address on p 176).

Margaret and Jim

'We thoroughly enjoyed the art class – it was a good start for us, providing a gentle interest and a new group of friends.'

Transport

As recovery continues, you and your relative may want to venture further away from home, perhaps for a shopping trip or a hospital appointment, but this can present travel problems if driving is restricted or not comfortable. Schemes are available in most areas, run by local authorities and voluntary organisations, providing transport for older and disabled people, with their carers as escorts. The journey is usually free or subsidised, depending on personal circumstances. Fares to hospital can be reimbursed for certain categories of people (see p 110).

The main schemes that help people with transport are listed below.

- Dial-a-Ride and Community Transport Schemes provide door-to-door service for shopping or similar outings for people who cannot use public transport. (Addresses on pp 166 and 167.)
- Hospital Car Schemes are usually run by the ambulance service and arranged through GPs' surgeries. They are available only for people who have a medical condition and cannot get to the hospital independently; one companion is usually allowed.
- The Orange Badge Scheme provides a national arrangement of parking concessions for people with severe walking difficulties who travel as drivers or passengers. Apart from the Cities of London and Westminster, the London Borough of Kensington and Chelsea and part of the London Borough of Camden, badge holders are exempt from certain parking restrictions – including free parking at on-street parking meters and for up to two hours on single and double yellow lines in England and Wales. Badges are issued for a three-year period through social services departments.
- Motability is a charity set up to help disabled people who want to spend the mobility component of their Disability Living Allowance or War Pensioner's Mobility Supplement on a car, scooter or wheelchair. Vehicles may be purchased or leased, and help may be available with the cost of special adaptations. A relative, friend or carer may apply and drive on behalf of a disabled person. (Address on p 171.)
- Disabled Persons Railcard Office have a railcard that offers concessionary fares to different categories of people, giving up to one-third off a range of rail tickets. An application form and booklet called *Rail Travel for Disabled Passengers* can be

obtained at most staffed stations or from the address on page 168. All rail operators give extra help to older or disabled travellers, particularly if they have advance notice.

■ Shopmobility schemes provide free wheelchair/scooter loan services in many town centres for anyone with a mobility problem. Users can usually park free or be met at the bus station or taxi rank by prior arrangement. An escort service is often available for people who are visually impaired or wheelchair users.

■ Taxicard (or similar name) is a service providing subsidised taxi fares; it is run by some larger councils for disabled people who are unable to use public transport. One passenger may accompany the cardholder. Ask at your local council office.

■ Tripscope offers a nationwide travel and transport information and advice service for older and disabled people (address on p 175).

■ The Community Transport Association has services to benefit providers of transport for people with mobility problems (address on p 166).

■ The DLA Unit of the Department of Social Security (address on p 176, under 'Vehicle Excise Duty') provides information about exemption from road tax for vehicles used exclusively by or for disabled people receiving the higher rate of the mobility component of Disability Living Allowance (DLA) or War Pensioners' Mobility Supplement. You may claim on behalf of the person you look after by completing an application form from the Benefits Agency.

For more *i*nformation

i Age Concern Factsheet 26 *Travel information for older people*.

i The local authority, for information about local schemes to help with transport.

Holidays

Joan

'We always planned our holiday so that I felt comfortable knowing how to reach a doctor – I kept the telephone numbers handy.'

Planning and organising holidays using a holiday service that is specially geared to deal with disabled people can take away much of the stress. The organisations listed below are selected from the many companies that provide help. Additional information is available from HELPBOX (see end of chapter).

For more *i*nformation

i Across Trust provides accompanied holidays and pilgrimages for sick and disabled people by means of a jumbo-ambulance. Individual or group applications are welcome. (Address on p 163.)

i Age Concern Factsheet 4 *Holidays for older people.*

i Air Transport Users Council publishes a booklet *Flight Plan*, which has a section for disabled passengers. (Address on p 163.)

i Holiday Care Service provides information and advice on holidays, travel facilities and respite care for people with disabilities, on low income or with special needs. A reservation helpline and holiday insurance information for disabled people are also available. (Address on p 170.)

i RADAR (Royal Association for Disability and Rehabilitation) provides information about many aspects of disability, including accessible destinations for holidays. (Address on p 173.)

i Special Families Home Swap Register produces a quarterly register to enable physically disabled people to swap their home for breaks elsewhere in the country. The homes listed are suitably equipped to accommodate people with physical disabilities. A small fee is charged for registration but there are no other costs (accommodation is free). (Address on p 174.)

■ Winged Fellowship provides respite care and holidays for physically disabled people, with or without a partner, in purpose-built holiday centres and on overseas and touring holidays. Trained staff and volunteers provide care. (Address on p 176.)

Conclusion

Celia, *an occupational therapist*
'Having a heart attack results in many changes – rise to the challenge!'

This chapter has encouraged you to focus on some of the inevitable changes that are taking place for you and your relative, and has offered some hints about how to accept the changes and move forward. Adjusting to a new situation is never straightforward, and it can be very stressful if the event that triggered the change was upsetting and beyond your control. We all deal with problems better if we feel that there is an element of choice involved and if we can retain some control over the situation. After a while the memory of unpleasant events will fade and you and your relative will be able to move forward with confidence and benefit from changes in life-style. Chapter 6 provides an insight into causes of stress and offers some techniques to help you both cope while you adjust.

For more *i*nformation

ⓘ The Disability Living Centres Council will tell you of the Centre nearest you, where you can see and try out aids and equipment (address on p 167).

ⓘ The Disabled Living Foundation provides information and advice about all aspects of daily living for people with disability (address on p 167).

ⓘ 'Family Doctor' booklets *Understanding Cholesterol and Heart Disease* and *A Survivor's Guide to Healthy Living* are available from most pharmacist/chemist shops.

i HELPBOX is a computer database that holds a vast range of health-related information (address on p 169).

i Hospital trusts often have health promotion departments that keep health-related information and employ trained advisers – look in the telephone directory under the Health Trust or Health Authority section.

i The Health Education Authority (address on p 169) provides details of a wide range of leaflets and books promoting good health. *Enjoy Healthy Eating* and *The Health Guide* are available at your GP's surgery.

4 How to cope with failing health

However well you care for your relative, their heart disease may begin to get worse. It is never possible to make forecasts about how an illness will develop or how long each stage will last but if the person is older it is inevitable that their health will eventually fail. You may wish to deal with the emotional side of this knowledge alone or ask for support, but many of the practical difficulties will be the same for all carers.

This chapter provides information to help you make early plans that will make life easier further along the road. It may seem difficult and even wrong to start thinking about failing health before that time has come but many families say it's less stressful to make decisions and deal with events if they have had time to think about the future and come to terms with changing circumstances.

Caring for an ill person at home can be a difficult undertaking and usually creates a mixture of emotions. Carers experience tremendous reward coupled with extreme tiredness; they feel anxiety and sadness and frequently become frustrated at the inadequacies of the 'system'. Despite this range of hurdles it is possible to overcome the practical problems and most carers feel determined to provide quality care at home for as long as possible.

There are no right or wrong decisions nor are there effortless ways of dealing with the position – simply do the best you can.

What is heart failure?

'Heart failure' is the name given to the characteristic signs and symptoms that develop when the heart is damaged and can no longer pump blood around the body in sufficient quantities to keep the organs working normally. The most noticeable effects are:

- loss of energy;
- tiredness after moderate exercise or even at rest;
- severe breathlessness;
- swelling of the ankles, feet and abdomen.

The heart can be damaged by a number of diseases, the most common of which is narrowing of the coronary arteries that supply oxygen and other nutrients to the heart muscle. In severe cases this can lead to a heart attack and affect the pumping action of the heart. As the performance of the heart deteriorates, blood pressure falls, the blood vessels narrow and the kidneys automatically retain fluids in the body to try to maintain the blood pressure level. This is a difficult balance to achieve and often an over-correction occurs: too much water floods the system and leaks out of the blood vessels into the tissues, causing the characteristic swelling of the feet, ankles and abdomen, and tissues over the base of the spine in someone who sits or lies rather than being mobile and walking about. Extra fluid builds up in the lungs, making breathing difficult. At first this is noticeable only during exercise but, as the heart grows weaker, the breathing is affected at rest – even in bed. In some cases the breathlessness is aggravated by a cough. In addition, the constriction of small blood vessels leads to an insufficient blood supply to the kidneys and other organs, reducing their ability to function satisfactorily.

It is unlikely that heart failure will occur immediately after a heart attack, because the heart is amazingly strong. Over the years, though, its performance weakens and heart failure comes on gradually. This gradual deterioration can also occur with other heart problems, such as heart muscle failure (cardiomyopathy), continual high blood pressure or valvular heart disease. Once the efficiency of the heart has started to fail, the process tends to speed up with the severity of the disease.

Diagnosis

In order to make a diagnosis the doctor will take a medical history to find out about any previous heart problems and other illnesses that give similar signs and symptoms. Breathlessness is common in people who have respiratory problems – for example, because they smoke heavily, who are obese or who have severe anaemia; and ankle swelling is a symptom of varicose veins (see p 7).

The doctor will make a physical examination to estimate whether the heart is enlarged; look for signs of blood congestion in the veins of the neck; check the heart rate and rhythm; and listen to how the heart sounds. Tests that confirm the diagnosis include:

■ an electrocardiogram (ECG) (see p 14);
■ a ultrasound scan (see p 14);
■ an echo-cardiogram – a painless test that gives visual pictures of the heart in action;
■ a chest X-ray to show the size and position of the heart.

Treatment has a much better effect if the problem is diagnosed early and your relative adapts to a slower pace of life, causing less strain on the heart.

Treatment

Doctors will plan treatment for heart failure by investigating the original problem. If it is caused by high blood pressure, thyroid gland problems or faulty heart valves, the symptoms can be improved with medication or surgery, or a combination of both. Unfortunately, not all forms of heart failure can be prevented or cured, because the deterioration often cannot be reversed. For example, any narrowing of the arteries that has already occurred in coronary heart disease cannot be changed; once the heart begins to fail, no further treatment of the arteries will help. However, the outlook is not entirely bleak, because treatments for heart failure have improved considerably over the years. As discussed in Chapters 1 and 3, symptoms can be relieved through medication and changes in life-style – the most important are stopping smoking, improving the diet, taking moderate exercise and reducing overweight. Your relative's doctor will recommend and explain any changes that will help the problem.

Medication is the most common treatment used to improve the performance of the heart and ease the unpleasant symptoms:

- **digoxin** (digitalis) to steady and strengthen the heart beat;
- **vasodilators** (ACE inhibitors) to improve the flow of blood through the blood vessels;
- **diuretics** (water tablets) to increase the output of urine, in order to reduce swelling in the tissues and thus improve breathlessness and pressure from swollen ankles.

If heart failure does not respond to medical treatment in a younger patient, the possibility of a heart transplant (cardiac transplantation) can be considered.

Problems arising from treatment

Everyone taking medication for heart failure receives regular check-ups because drug treatment carries risks of side (unwanted) effects. The most common side effects are related to too little potassium in the blood stream from excess water loss due to the water tablets and the effects of the ACE inhibitors. Loss of potassium leads to tiredness and an irregular heart beat. Excess digoxin can build up in the body, causing nausea and a slow pulse rate. Finally, the vasodilators can lower the blood pressure too much, causing some dizziness.

If the doctor suspects that medication is causing unwanted side effects, blood tests can be done to check the drug levels in the system. If you or your relative have any concerns about possible side effects of treatment, do discuss this with the doctor promptly, because it can take a while to stabilise treatments and the state of the heart itself may alter. If the problems remain untreated or changes in symptoms develop, the heart failure will continue to get worse, resulting in quite marked distress. But *never* stop any medication without speaking to the doctor first.

Local support services

Support for your relative and for you as a carer may be available locally from a number of sources run by statutory, private and voluntary organisations. Most of these services will be accessed via the NHS or the social services departments, depending on whether the care your relative requires is assessed either as 'health' or 'nursing' care or as 'social' care. There may seem to be little difference in practical terms and in reality the two services work very closely together. 'Nursing' care is provided by NHS staff and is given when someone has medical needs; 'social' care is provided by social services and is available for personal needs such as washing, dressing and help getting to the toilet. Both agencies may use contract workers. Your relative can purchase all their care needs from private agencies if they are willing to pay the charges or, in a few specific instances, if their local authority agrees to give them 'direct payments' to pay directly for the social services they have assessed to be needed. In many areas, additional services are offered by voluntary organisations; for example, Age Concern and other caring organisations run day-care centres and other facilities.

Do you need help?

Joan

'Someone showed me a book about services for carers after Peter had died. I had never realised that there were so many organisations that provide help and support.'

Look at the checklist below. If you answer 'yes' to any of the questions and would like further information, you should ask for help locally. Ask at your GP's surgery, health centre or social services office.

- Have you just started to care for someone else?
- Do you think the person you care for should have an assessment or re-assessment of their needs?
- Do you want to talk to someone about how you feel and what help you are entitled to receive?
- Would you like to know more about respite care facilities?
- Do you feel exhausted and close to breaking point?
- Do you need help to move your relative safely – for both of your sakes?
- Do you think extra equipment would help you to manage better?
- Do you feel that you could have received a better quality service or better support from those providing care?

Rani, *a district nurse*

'If you are unsure about caring, speak to your district nurse. We know all about local services and you don't always have to get the doctor to refer you.'

Although you may have been caring for a while, it is possible that you are not familiar with the full range of local services. Why not find out now what help is available, before pressure builds up and you reach crisis point. District nurses or social workers are thought by many people to be a last point of call when a crisis has arisen, but they can give support and advice to carers long before that stage is reached. The assessment process and how it can help you and your relative are described in Chapter 2. It's the key to all types of care and is open to anyone who feels they are in need of a support service. Getting extra help does not mean that you have failed or that you are receiving charity.

Care options

Social services care at home

Facilities vary around the country, so you will need to find out what services are provided or arranged by the local authority where your relative lives; for example, this could be a county council, unitary council, metropolitan borough or a London borough. If your relative does not meet the social services department's criteria for care at the outset, information should be available about other people and groups who can be contacted. Social services departments should work closely with other agencies to provide the most suitable care for both your needs and those of your relative, and should review the situation as circumstances change. Help for adults generally includes assistance with day-to-day living in their own homes. For example:

- personal care (eg washing, toileting, going to bed);
- practical help (eg housework or shopping);
- help for carers who may be partners, relatives or friends (eg respite care);
- advice and equipment from an occupational therapist (eg commode, bed raisers);
- help for people who need care from specialist staff (eg those with hearing or sight loss, or physical disabilities).

In order to meet the needs of people who prefer to receive care at home, social services departments may provide – either direct or through a contract with an independent agency – specially trained care assistants who come to the house as required. Care assistants give personal (hygiene) care only, such as washing and toileting; they are not trained nurses, so do not undertake other kinds of body care such as changing a catheter. Unfortunately, funding is scarce in most areas so the level of personal care your relative receives will be determined by eligibility criteria (see p 37) and by the amount of money available, and might be less than you would wish. (See p 39 for information about appealing against a decision of the social services department.)

Health services (NHS)

Services from the NHS for people with long-term health care needs range from special equipment to rehabilitation, respite health care and NHS continuing inpatient care – ie care that the NHS pays for in full. Each health authority sets its own criteria for these services, based on national guidance (HSG(95)8 *NHS Responsibilities for Meeting Continuing Health Care Needs*; NHS MEL(1996)22 in Scotland). They must be published and should be available from the local health authority. Your relative's health care needs will be assessed against these criteria.

If an NHS patient is receiving treatment in hospital and will need services after discharge, an assessment of their needs should be carried out before leaving hospital. This should involve staff from both the health and the social services, and take into account the wishes of the patient and of their family and carers. The consultant (or the GP in some community hospitals) decides whether the patient's assessed needs meet the criteria for any of the continuing health care services. If the decision is 'No', the patient, their family, carer or someone else (perhaps someone from the local community health council) has the right to ask the health authority to review the decision. The right applies only to NHS patients in hospital.

Hospitals should have information about how to ask for a review and about how discharge from hospital should be handled. In addition, patients, their families and carers should be given information in writing (or in other appropriate formats) about the health and social care services they have been assessed as needing, including details of any charges for services from the social services department. If you wish to know more about the appeals procedure relating to continuing health care, ask for information from the ward sister or at your local community health council (see p 102). A representative of the community health council can help prepare your case.

The District Nursing Service operates throughout the country, providing nursing treatment and health care for people who remain at home. District nurses are based at GP surgeries and health centres; patients are usually referred by their GPs, but anyone can contact a district nurse direct. Ask for a telephone number at your surgery or leave a message for the nurse. They are a great source of local information about resources and can put you in touch with other services and arrange for equipment and items such as incontinence pads. Telephone for an assessment if you feel you need help and advice. Don't wait until you are desperate, particularly if your relative has become incontinent.

Laura

'I felt so relieved when the district nurses came to us. They turned my husband at regular hours and he never got any sore patches.'

For more *i*nformation

- ❶ Age Concern Factsheet 32 *Disability and ageing: your rights to social services.*

- ❶ Age Concern Factsheet 37 *Hospital discharge arrangements, and NHS continuing health care services.*

Independent care providers – help at home

Help at home is also available from private and voluntary agencies that offer a range of services, including personal and domestic care, respite facilities, holiday accommodation and companionship. One such organisation, Crossroads Care (see p 92), has schemes in most areas of the country. Charges made by independent care providers vary and may be greater than the rates charged by social services. If you wish to obtain care from an independent agency for your relative, or to top up the amount of care they receive from the local authority, ask your social worker for details or look in Yellow Pages or check with a national organisation such as those listed in the section 'For more information'. Some independent agencies belong to organisations that require them to meet certain standards, such as those set by the United Kingdom Home Care Association (UKHCA). Lists of independent agencies that meet any service standards specified by local authorities in their contracts for care at home may be available from their registration and inspection unit (see p 90). It's worth asking about registration so that you understand what checks are made on independent agencies. Local authorities have the power to inspect any community care services that they contract but are not obliged to do so, nor for any providers of day care.

Residential and nursing homes

Christine

'My father went into a home and he was given good care. But we visited several homes before we found one that he felt was right for him.'

Residential and nursing homes offer permanent accommodation to people who are unable to live independently in the community. This includes disabled people and frail older people, including those with dementia. Many homes also offer respite care facilities and other temporary places.

At the outset of caring you and your relative may be coping well and may not wish to consider these as an option. However, over a period of time, if the care situation becomes stressed or your relative's health deteriorates, moving into a care home may become the best or only choice open to you both. In such a situation, it's vital that everyone involved in the decision has a chance to express their feelings about seeking permanent care. Discuss with your relative the merits of staying at home or entering residential care, and weigh up the possible advantages and disadvantages for everyone concerned. Think about all the factors that might influence the final decision:

■ the benefit of increased safety and care provide by trained staff;

■ peace of mind and less stress for the carer, especially if relationships have become strained;

■ ready-made companionship – but loss of privacy and independence;

■ feelings of guilt and the loss of a close relative from the immediate family circle;

■ the costs of travel and time;

■ the difficulty finding a suitable home;

■ the overall cost of residential care set against charges for care at home (include Attendance Allowance in your calculations for care at home – see p 105);

■ however, could your relative continue to live at home or in sheltered or 'extra care' housing if the level of services were increased?

Taking the discussion a stage further

It is not easy to decide which type of home to live in and the decision should not be made hurriedly. A list of addresses can be obtained from the local authority, and details can then be obtained direct from the individual homes.

Gill

'As my husband's illness got worse, we had a family conference about what would be the best thing to do. We all wanted to keep him at home with us.'

Residential homes (whether run by statutory bodies, voluntary organisations or the private sector) offer living accommodation but do not provide nursing care. Local authority residential homes have to be inspected by the local authority inspection and registration unit. Those in the private or voluntary sector that care for four or more residents must be registered and are inspected twice a year; 'small' residential homes in the private and voluntary sector are also registered but under a simpler system.

Nursing homes provide nursing and medical care for people who need greater individual attention; they are all inspected and registered by the health authority. The NHS owns a few nursing homes – which are exempt from registration.

Dual-registered homes provide both residential and nursing/medical care, and have to be registered and inspected by both the health and the local authority units. Both inspection reports must be publicly available. It could be worth considering this sort of home, if your relative might need to move from one type to the other. It is also worth bearing in mind that, at some point in the future, your relative might still need to move to another home if they come to need more specialist care.

Ask around among your friends and acquaintances about the care homes you are considering. Word of mouth is often a useful source of information and a measure of local feeling. When your relative is getting closer to making a decision, gather together local details, draw up a short-list and arrange to visit the homes. It's important to get a feel for the atmosphere and the care provided. If possible, see if you and your relative can visit to share a meal or other activities with the current residents. You might want to ask yourselves some questions to help assess what type of home would be best:

- How mobile is your relative?
- What is your relative's current physical and mental state, and is this likely to change rapidly?
- How much care is needed – round the clock cover or day-time support only?
- What type of care is needed – nursing care including medication and treatments or just personal hygiene?
- Will special aids and equipment be needed?

Remember also the things that your relative likes to do or feels are important. For example, being able to attend church, favourite meals, having regular visitors or playing bridge.

For more *i*nformation

ⓘ Carers Handbook series: *Finding and paying for residential and nursing home care* by Marina Lewycka, published by Age Concern Books.

ⓘ Age Concern Factsheet 10 *Local authority charging procedures for residential and nursing home care.*

ⓘ Age Concern Factsheet 29 *Finding residential and nursing home accommodation.*

ⓘ Age Concern Factsheet 39 *Paying for care in a residential or nursing home if you have a partner.*

ⓘ Age Concern Factsheet 40 *Transfer of assets and paying for care in a residential or nursing home.*

ⓘ *Care Homes Directory*: updated annually, it contains details of over 1,000 nursing, residential and respite care homes. Published by HOMES Directories Ltd (Valley Court, Croydon, Royston, Hertfordshire SG6 0HE).

ⓘ *Directory of Hospice & Palliative Care Services 1997.* Published by The Hospice Information Service (address on page 170).

ⓘ Elderly Accommodation Council (address on p 168).

ⓘ Independent Healthcare Association (address on p 170).

ⓘ Jewish Care (address on p 171).

ⓘ United Kingdom Home Care Association (UKHCA) (address on p 175).

ⓘ For registration and inspection units, look in the local telephone directory or ask at your social services department or health authority.

Respite care

Gill

'Having a break was difficult. I felt guilty about leaving my husband although he said he was fine. He did miss me, but after a break I felt ready to carry on for a bit longer.'

All carers need a break from caring, to be alone or to spend time with other family members and friends. This type of break is called 'respite care' and can take many forms:

- a couple of hours out to do some shopping, read a magazine or visit a friend;
- a longer period to go away on a week-end break or a holiday;
- time spent at home catching up on jobs while your relative goes to a day centre;
- an uninterrupted night's sleep.

Breaks like these are not a luxury – they are essential for your own health and well-being and will help you to cope better. Your relative might also welcome a break from the usual environment or routine. Everyone needs to 'recharge their batteries' and ease the stressed load, so, even if you feel fine at present, try not to leave it until you are desperate for a break before attempting to make arrangements. Respite care can always be organised if there is an emergency, but it's much better to have a regular time set aside that enables you to plan ahead and have something to look forward to. The energy needed to organise a break might be more than you can take on if you are at crisis point.

You might be doubtful about handing the care of your relative over to someone else, even for an hour or so, but remember that the break will be good for both of you. A social worker or district nurse can help you make arrangements or you can contact one of the national agencies listed below. Try to involve your relative in making the arrangements, if at all possible. For example, if there is more than one option, your relative might want to make the choice.

- **BNA** (British Nursing Association) provides care assistants, 'home helps' and qualified nurses to care for individual people in their own homes. A wide range of services is offered, including convalescent care, night care, personal care, shopping, companionship and respite care. The organisation caters for every level of need from occasional visits to live-in care. Look in the telephone directory for a local number or contact them at the address on page 164.
- **Crossroads Care schemes** are part of a national network set up to provide practical help and support to older and disabled people and their carers. Each situation is assessed individually, the trained care attendant taking over the role of the family carer. Using the Crossroads scheme will give you an opportunity for a respite break at a time of your choosing; care is given 365 days of the year. Look in the telephone directory for a local number or contact them at the address on page 167.

Charges are usually made for respite care; each organisation will give you details according to your relative's circumstances. If regular respite care is part of your relative's care from social services, ask them what charges, if any, there might be. People who meet their health authority's criteria for NHS respite health care may have this provided in a hospital. (There is no charge for respite health care from the NHS.)

Day care

Gill

'The ambulance came once a week to take Bob to the day centre, until his health began to fail. He didn't mind going because he realised that I could go out and have my hair cut and have a break. The social worker set it up for us.'

Day care for your relative is another way for you to have time to yourself, and for your relative to enjoy other activities and different company. All local authorities and many voluntary organisations offer day-care facilities at specially run day centres. Some services are provided in purpose-built day centres whereas others share accommodation in community centres or residential homes. All offer support to carers and older people, and cover a range of needs from social activities and lunch through to specialist care. Your relative can receive chiropody, hair dressing, a bath if this is difficult at home, sit quietly and doze, or chat to staff and other users. The staff are trained care assistants with additional volunteer help in many centres. For more details, ask your social worker or district nurse.

Laundry services

> ### *Laura*
>
> 'The district nurse said that my husband was eligible for incontinence pads and the boxes arrived at the door. The pads made such a difference because I had less washing and my husband slept better because he stopped worrying about wetting the bed.'

If your relative is incontinent, excellent help can be found in most areas through the Continence Advisory Service. Ask at your relative's GP surgery for details. A district nurse or continence adviser will make an assessment. Incontinence has many causes, and it may be possible to improve the symptoms considerably with treatment.

For people who have heavy urine and soiling problems, incontinence pads are available and it may be possible to make use of a home collection laundry service. Facilities vary around the country.

For more *i*nformation

i Age Concern Factsheet 23 *Help with incontinence.*

Meals-on-wheels

A meals service is provided for many older or disabled people. It is run by the Women's Royal Voluntary Service and other local organisations, and these reasonably priced meals can be delivered either hot daily or as a pre-packed frozen service at regular intervals. Referral is usually via a healthcare professional or the social services/social work department.

Extra equipment

One of the main problems encountered by carers when they nurse someone at home concern the difficulties that arise as the person becomes less mobile. Immobility for people suffering from heart disease tends to develop gradually as their health and strength fail – unlike the abruptness of paralysis immediately following a stroke – so for you and your relative each stage can be assessed and you can adjust to whatever degree of movement remains. Aids and equipment to help with moving and handling patients are used frequently by professional carers nowadays as part of Health and Safety regulations. The most useful pieces of equipment to ask about are:

- **wheelchair:** the effort required to walk even short distances may create unnecessary isolation, especially if breathing is difficult, so for mobility inside and outside the house a wheelchair is essential;
- **urine bottle/bedpan:** nowadays many people prefer to purchase these items from a pharmacist/chemist shop, but bedpans can be borrowed or hired if required;
- **commode:** this piece of 'furniture' is necessary in the later stages of an illness but can also be useful if your relative needs to use the toilet during the night;
- **sliding sheets:** made of a slippery nylon fabric, the two surfaces slide easily when placed together to move a person in any direction on chairs, beds and car seats;
- **lifting aids (hand held):** these firm, flat, plastic supports can be placed under the thighs or the back of an individual and held by two people to make lifting in a chair or bed easier. Alternatively, a curved banana-shaped board can be placed

between a chair and the bed (or wheelchair) to slide the individual across so that they do not have to be raised into a standing position. Using aids such as these puts less strain on frail limbs and shoulder joints – for both the individual and their carers;

- **mechanical hoists:** these operate by electricity or hydraulic power and are used mainly in a private or nursing home setting by professional carers for people who are very difficult to move;
- **bed and chair raisers:** these look like heavy-duty plastic flowerpots and are excellent for raising furniture by several inches to ease the strain of bending and moving;
- **sheepskins and special mattresses:** several types are available to help protect vulnerable pressure points when a person becomes chair- or bed-ridden;
- **pillow support or back rest:** several types are available;
- **handrails and ramps:** these can be positioned at various places, such as the bathroom and at the entrances to the house;
- **adapted cutlery and crockery:** for general eating and drinking, or for kitchen use if your relative enjoys helping with the cooking or wants to make a hot drink;
- **two-way 'baby listening' system, portable telephone, answering machine or entryphone:** all of these offer a means of communication without the need to rush.

Laura

'The commode was brilliant. It had wheels and we could push it right over the toilet seat, so there was no need to waste energy struggling to move in a small space.'

In all areas of the country equipment can be hired or borrowed from several organisations; the main providers are social services, NHS trusts and voluntary organisations. Your first point of call for information and assessment is an occupational therapist (OT). They work towards restoring and maintaining levels of independence and reducing the impact of illness. Occupational therapists may be based with social services or the NHS, depending on whether your relative has been referred to them because of a health or a social need. Ask your doctor to make a referral for a home visit if you are unsure which agency to approach. Equipment supplied by the NHS is lent free of charge. Unfortunately, the waiting lists are long in many areas.

Grants are available through local authorities if you need help with major adaptations to your home, such as a stairlift or adapting a bathroom. An assessment for this is made by an occupational therapist.

For more *i*nformation

❶ The Disabled Living Foundation offers advice on aids and equipment (address on p 167).

❶ The Disability Living Centres Council (address on p 167) can tell you the centre nearest you, where you can see and try out aids and equipment.

❶ The local branches of the British Red Cross or St John Ambulance give advice and arrange the hire or loan of equipment – look in the telephone directory for a contact number, or ask the district nurse for a referral.

❶ Many pharmacist/chemist shops sell aids and small pieces of equipment or keep catalogues for mail order.

❶ Care and Repair provide advice and practical help to older and disabled people and those on low incomes, to help them improve their home conditions. Charges are made, but these can be set against a grant if one is provided. (Address on p 165.)

Terminal care

Gill

'Somehow I felt less upset when my husband died at home because we were in our own house. I know that not everyone can manage care at home, but I had lots of help from the district nurses and my family.'

Reg

'My wife was moved to a hospice just before she died. I couldn't care for her as well as the nurses because she needed constant attention. She was looked after so well I felt I had made the right decision.'

Caring for a relative with a terminal illness at home is a time of great emotional and physical strain. It is not easy to make predictions about how long the final stages of an illness will last or how much care a person may need. People whose health is deteriorating have good and bad days and may remain on a plateau for quite a while, supported by medication and nursing care, before they finally slip into unconsciousness. If you are continuing to nurse your relative at home in the final stages of their illness, you will be offered support from the local district nursing team. They assess how much care is needed and will visit several times a day to wash and turn your relative. In some areas there are special flexible services that provide help to settle patients down at night and give pain-killing and sedative drugs, and all-night nursing services to sit with very ill people. Your relative's doctor will make the necessary arrangements or you can contact a district nurse direct if the service is available for your use.

As the time approaches when your relative is dying you may be concerned about what to do and how you will cope. Try to bring yourself to talk to a nurse about this and let them advise you about what steps you need to take. Being with a loved one who dies at home can be a very tranquil experience, knowing that you have helped them die peacefully in their own surroundings. If your relative needs to be admitted to hospital or a hospice for their last days, the staff will do everything possible to make them and your family feel comfortable. Ask the staff to let you help with the care, so that you can remain involved and continue to do your best for your relative.

For more *i*nformation

ℹ️ Carers Handbook series: *Caring for someone who is dying* by Penny Mares, published by Age Concern Books.

Conclusion

The decision whether to look after your relative at home or arrange care in a nursing home will be based on a number of factors – the wishes of the person concerned; your ability to give quality care; the support that other family members can give; and the type and amount of care that is needed. It's not an easy decision and cannot be taken lightly. Caring for someone is a time-consuming and strenuous job that draws heavily on the personal resources of the main carer. This task is almost impossible to undertake single-handed and relies on the support of the professional services as well as family and friends. If the care is long term, it can put a strain on marriages and stretch finances.

Whatever your initial decision may be, it is important that you review it from time to time and accept that no carer can ever make a promise that is binding forever.

The next chapter will help you to deal with the affairs of the person you care for.

5 Dealing with everyday affairs

NEWCASTLE-UNDER-LYME
COLLEGE LIBRARY

One of the main roles of a carer is that of helping to manage the financial and legal affairs of their relative. This may be because they have become too physically disabled or mentally confused to manage alone, or because they feel unsure about dealing with people in 'authority' and feel reluctant to take decisions alone about complex issues. You might have to take over responsibility gradually or swiftly, depending on the state of health and wishes of your relative.

This chapter outlines the services and agencies you could turn to for help and describes some of the welfare benefits and legal procedures that you and your relative may wish to investigate.

Dealing with the affairs of another person is a serious business and you may feel daunted at first. However, there are people who will help and advise you and there are many safeguards in place to protect you and your relative. It would be wise to cover yourself by seeking advice from a reputable source – a solicitor, an accountant, a bank or a voluntary organisation – before you enter into legal contracts or make any major decisions, especially concerning property or the management of your relative's money.

> ### *Sylvia*
>
> 'After my husband had a heart attack I took over the financial planning –
> I soon got the hang of bank statements and the bank helped me set up
> monthly payments for all our main bills.'

Finding out about help and advice

Getting the right information needs mental stamina, creative
thinking and a mind that can jump like a grasshopper – or so it
feels on occasions, particularly if you are tied to the house. Look
out for sound, informative articles published by the local and
national press and programmes broadcast on radio and television.
The material is often well researched, unbiased and aimed at the
general public. For more detailed information, advice and advocacy
there are many organisations that offer carers a service at local
and national level; some are specialists in their field and others
provide general information and act as signposts to the specialists.
Most organisations offer facilities for disabled people and some
information in minority languages. The main agencies to contact
are listed in the Table on the next three pages.

> ### *Elsie*
>
> 'Tom had always done the paperwork at home, so when he wasn't up to
> it I asked for some financial advice at the Citizens Advice Bureau – they
> helped me fill out our tax form.'

State benefits and grants

The benefits system is complex and can only be covered broadly
here because each person has individual needs and the information,
amounts given and eligibility are subject to change. The range of
benefits is listed in leaflets available from the Benefits Agency,

Organisation	Services offered	How to contact
Advocacy services	An advocacy service (advocate) will represent and speak on behalf of people who are not skilled or confident to do so themselves, to help them to obtain and make best use of local services	Local telephone directory or ask at Citizens Advice Bureau
Age Concern	Provides information (eg Information Line), support, practical help, social activities and a range of publications for older people and carers	Local telephone directory or address on page 177. Information Line: 0800 00 99 66
Benefits Agency	Provides information on all state welfare benefits and processes most local claims	Local telephone directory
Benefits Enquiry Freephone Line	Provides general advice, information, claim forms and leaflets for disabled people and their carers by telephone or post, but cannot deal with individual claims	Tel: 0800 88 22 00 Textphone: 0800 24 33 55
Citizens Advice Bureau	Free, confidential advice and information on a wide range of legal, financial, social and consumer problems, and help with form filling and representation at hearings	Local telephone directory

continued

101

Organisation	Services offered	How to contact
Community health council (health council in Scotland)	Free, independent organisation that monitors health services at a local level and represents the interests of people who may have concerns about NHS care	Local telephone directory
Consumer services departments	Offer information to local people about the services and facilities available from their own organisation. They are usually provided by all statutory agencies (eg local councils, health trusts and social services departments) and many services industries (eg water, gas and electricity)	Local telephone directory under appropriate agency
Counsel and Care	Provides free counselling, information and advice for older people and carers, including specialist advice about using independent agencies; publishes a range of factsheets and administers trust funds that make payments for equipment and respite care	Address on page 166
Disability Information Services (called DIAL in some areas)	Advice on aids and equipment, telephone and services	Local telephone directory
Disability Living Centres	Have aids and equipment you can see and try out	Address on page 167

continued

102

Organisation	Services offered	How to contact
Disabled Living Foundation	Information on aids and equipment	Address on page 167
Help the Aged	Provides a range of services, including telephone lines for Winter Warmth, SeniorLine (a free information helpline) and SeniorLink (an emergency telephone system)	Address on page 169
Housing Advice	Many local authorities provide a housing advice service to local residents in owner-occupied or rented accommodation	Local telephone directory
Independent Advice Centres	Independent organisations in most urban areas and some rural areas, offering free advice on problems relating to benefits, debt and work issues	Federation of Independent Advice Centres (p 168) or local telephone directory
Neighbourhood Schemes	Many local authorities and voluntary groups run community schemes offering a range of information and support to local people	Local telephone directory under 'Council'
Public library	Excellent sources of local information, books, videos, directories, quality journals and many daily newspapers	Personal visit, telephone, or limited home delivery

most local authorities, the Citizens Advice Bureaux and some post offices. Useful ones to look out for are:

- Benefits Agency leaflet FB2 *Which Benefit?*
- Benefits Agency leaflet FB31 *Caring for Someone*, which includes carers' benefits.
- Benefits Agency leaflet FB28 *Sick or Disabled?*
- Benefits Agency leaflet IS1 *Income Support*.
- Employment Service leaflet JSAL5 *JobSeeker's Allowance*.

For telephone advice about claims and information, contact the local **Benefits Agency** office or the **Benefits Enquiry Freephone** (see p 101). If you need information about benefits in other languages, contact your local Benefits Agency office.

People claiming a state benefit must meet strict criteria; some benefits are means-tested or taxed or both. If you or your relative disagree with a decision made by the Benefits Agency, you have the right to appeal and ask for your case to be reviewed.

Jeff, *a benefits adviser*

'Ask about benefits or you won't know what is available. It's really worth getting a knowledgeable person to check out your circumstances. Ask for help at the Citizens Advice Bureau.'

Why people are reluctant to claim

There are millions of pounds of unclaimed benefits, particularly those targeted at older people; for example, Income Support, Council Tax Benefit and Attendance Allowance. Benefits advisers say that older people and carers are reluctant to claim means-tested benefits for lots of reasons:

- they think they are not eligible;
- they don't know what is available;
- they don't want to be bothered with the paperwork;
- they find the claim forms too complicated;
- they are too proud and believe that they may be taking money from someone else who is more deserving.

Many carers claim on behalf of a relative without realising that they might be eligible for benefits in their own right.

Maria, a benefits adviser

'Many older people and carers say that they feel trapped and at the end of their tether. They think that they can manage and continue to struggle when they might be entitled to make a claim.'

Benefits for the person you look after

Attendance Allowance

Attendance Allowance is for people aged 65 years or over who need help with personal care or someone to watch over them. It is tax-free and not means-tested but to qualify the person must normally have needed help with personal care for a period of six months. If Attendance Allowance is granted, it will be backdated to the date that the completed application forms are received by the Benefits Agency. People who are terminally ill qualify immediately. There are two rates, according to how much care is needed. Get a claim pack from the Benefits Agency (see p 101) or one of the advice agencies (eg the Citizens Advice Bureau), which will also be able to help your relative fill it in. (Leaflet DS 702)

Disability Living Allowance (DLA)

Disability Living Allowance is for people under 65 years of age who have needed care or had mobility difficulties for more than three months. It has a care component for people who need a lot of looking after, and a mobility component for people who need help with getting around. Disability Living Allowance is tax-free and not means-tested and not dependent on National Insurance contributions. The person receiving the allowance is free to spend the money however they choose; it does not have to be spent on care. The mobility component has two rates and the care component three; these are awarded according to the needs of the disabled person. People who are terminally ill qualify immediately for the highest rate of the care component. The Disability Living Allowance is a gateway to other types of help (eg the Orange Badge scheme, which gives holders special parking privileges). (Leaflet DS 704)

Incapacity Benefit (IB)

Incapacity Benefit is for people under state pension age who are unable to work because of an illness or disability and have paid enough National Insurance contributions. The benefit is given at different rates, depending on whether the illness or disability is likely to be short or long term. For the first 28 weeks a claimant is assessed on their ability to carry out their own job, based on information given on medical certificates provided by the GP. After 28 weeks the sick or disabled person is assessed on how well they can carry out a range of work-related activities, called an 'All Work Test'. This assessment is carried out through completion of a questionnaire by the claimant and possibly also an examination by an appointed doctor. Some people may qualify for extra money if their husband or wife is over 60 years or they have dependent children. (Leaflet IB 202)

Severe Disablement Allowance (SDA)

Severe Disablement Allowance is a tax-free benefit for people who have not been able to work for 28 consecutive weeks because of illness or disability but do not qualify for Incapacity Benefit because they have not paid enough National Insurance contributions. The claimant must pass the All Work Test for incapacity. (Leaflet NI 252)

Benefits for Carers

Invalid Care Allowance (ICA)

To qualify for Invalid Care Allowance you must be providing care for at least 35 hours per week to a person who is receiving Attendance Allowance *or* Constant Attendance Allowance *or* the middle or highest rates of the care component of Disability Living Allowance. You must be aged between 16 and 64 years when you first claim. You cannot get Invalid Care Allowance if you are in full-time education. You can have a job earning up to £50 per week (after deduction of allowable expenses – eg childcare) and still get Invalid Care Allowance. The allowance is taxable. You cannot claim it at the same time as some other benefits, such as Incapacity Benefit for yourself, and you must be the only carer of the invalid person claiming this benefit. Invalid Care Allowance can be back-dated for up to 52 weeks. (Leaflet DS 700)

Carer's Premium

This is an extra amount included in the calculation of your benefit if you claim Income Support, Housing Benefit or Council Tax Benefit. To qualify you must receive Invalid Care Allowance or meet the conditions for getting it but receive another benefit instead (eg Income Support). (Leaflet FB 31)

Home Responsibilities Protection

If you receive Invalid Care Allowance, you are entitled to National Insurance credits which will count towards your own pension. If you cannot claim Invalid Care Allowance for any reason but still care for over 35 hours per week for someone who receives Attendance Allowance, Constant Attendance Allowance or the high or middle rate of the care component of Disability Living Allowance, you can apply for Home Responsibilities Protection, which helps towards your qualifying for retirement pension. (Form CF 411)

General benefits

Income Support (IS)

Income Support is a means-tested benefit paid to someone aged 16 years or over whose income is below a certain level and who is not expected to sign on as unemployed. The person must be incapable of work because of sickness or disability, or bringing up children alone, or aged 60 years and over, or looking after a disabled person or registered blind. Some people who are not in these groups may also qualify for help: Income Support can be paid to top up other benefits or earnings from part-time work (including self-employment), provided they work for fewer than 16 hours per week or if they have no form of income, or they have not paid enough National Insurance contributions. Qualification for Income Support may be affected by the level of their savings. (Leaflet IS 1)

JobSeeker's Allowance

JobSeeker's Allowance has replaced Unemployment Benefit and Income Support for unemployed people looking for work. The allowance is paid to someone capable of working at least 40 hours per week who has paid sufficient National Insurance contributions or has income and savings below a certain level. The person must be resident in the UK, aged between 18 years and state pension age, and not in relevant education (eg a full-time student). Although the person must be essentially unemployed and actively seeking work, some income may be earned from part-time work before JobSeeker's Allowance is affected. People claiming this allowance enter into a JobSeeker's Agreement. When drawing up this agreement, the adviser at the Job Centre will take into account any part-time or voluntary work. (Leaflet JSAL 5)

Social Fund

The Social Fund provides discretionary grants and loans to help people with expenses that are difficult to pay for out of regular income. (Leaflets SFL 2 and SB 16)

Crisis Loans

Crisis Loans are for people with no savings or access to funds to help them cope with an emergency or disaster, such as fire or burglary, that puts the family at serious health or safety risk. Applicants do not have to be in receipt of other state benefits.

Cold Weather Payments

Cold weather payments are paid automatically to some recipients of Income Support, including pensioners and disabled people, when the actual or forecast average temperature goes down to freezing (zero degrees Celsius) or below for seven consecutive days.

Winter Fuel Payments

In November 1997 the Chancellor announced additional cash payments for pensioner households to help with fuel bills for two winters. Someone receiving Income Support or income-based Job-Seeker's Allowance (including one of the pensioner premiums) in the week beginning 5 January 1998 should have received £50 by the end of that January. A couple would have received a single payment between them. A person not getting Income Support that week but who was over pension age and receiving a retirement pension or certain other benefits such as Attendance Allowance should have received £20 if they were the only qualifying pensioner in the household or £10 if they live with one or more qualifying pensioners. Winter Fuel Payments are to be made again in the winter of 1998/99.

Funeral Payment

Help for funeral expenses is available to some people receiving means-tested benefits, who are responsible for the funeral of a partner, close relative or close friend. The payment may have to be repaid from any money or property left by the person who died. Any savings might affect how much the applicant gets, and the Benefits Agency must agree that it is reasonable for the person to be responsible for the funeral before they will agree any payment. (Leaflet D 49)

Widow's Benefits

Widows may qualify for one of three widows' benefits: **Widow's Payment** (an immediate tax-free lump sum); **Widowed Mother's**

Allowance; and **Widows' Pension**, if their husband had paid enough National Insurance contributions. (Leaflet NP 45)

Housing Benefit and Council Tax Benefit

These are worked out in a similar way to Income Support but are administered by the local authority (see below). Savings and some income may affect how much you or you relative can get. **Housing Benefit** helps tenants pay rent, and **Council Tax Benefit** helps tenants and home owners pay their Council Tax. People receiving Income Support and who claim Housing Benefit or Council Tax Benefit will generally automatically be awarded the maximum amounts. (Leaflet RR 2)

For more *i*nformation

i Age Concern Factsheet 16 *Income related benefits: income and capital.*

i Age Concern Factsheet 17 *Housing Benefit and Council Tax Benefit.*

i Age Concern Factsheet 18 *A brief guide to money benefits.*

i Age Concern Factsheet 25 *Income Support and the Social Fund.*

i Age Concern Factsheet 34 *Attendance Allowance and Disability Living Allowance.*

NHS benefits

A range of health-related benefits are available for people who receive other state benefits or are on a low income. These might help your relative with charges for prescriptions, eye tests and glasses, dentures and dental treatment, wigs and bandages, and with fares to hospital to receive NHS treatment. Some people (eg those receiving Income Support) are automatically exempted from some of these charges. Other people on a low income may get help if they apply on form **AG 1** (except for fares to hospital, which must be claimed from the hospital at each visit). Ask for details at your surgery, hospital clinic or a pharmacy.

Taxation

Inland Revenue

Home visits can be arranged for enquiries about personal income and other taxes if your relative is unable to get to a local office. A range of information is available in booklets, many of which appear in minority languages, Braille and large print, and in audio cassettes.

Council Tax

Council Tax, collected by local councils as a contribution towards local services, is assessed according to the value of each property and the number of adults in it. There are reductions, discounts and exemptions available that may help you as a carer and your relative. These relate to empty dwellings (you may have left your home to go and care for your relative or they may have moved in with you), to homes with substantial adaptations that are placed in a lower valuation band, and to people whose presence in a household is disregarded, thus leading to a lower bill. Once your Council Tax liability is assessed, you or your relative may be able to claim Council Tax Benefit (see above) to help pay. Get help from an advice agency (see the Table on p 101) or your local authority.

For more *i*nformation

i Age Concern Factsheet 15 *Income tax and older people*.

i Age Concern Factsheet 21 *Council Tax and older people*.

Grants from private organisations

Many local and national trusts and charities have grants to help you purchase one-off items of equipment or pay for respite care. For example, the Independent Living (1993) Fund (address on p 170) is intended for very severely disabled people who receive a substantial care package (over £200 per week) via social services; they may be eligible for money to buy in extra care if there is no one to fully meet their care needs. A number of criteria must be met.

For information about local and national grant-making organisations and trusts, try asking at the local Citizens Advice Bureau, parish council or public library, or contact Counsel and Care (address on p 166) or the National Association of Councils for Voluntary Service (address on p 172).

Managing somebody's financial affairs

There are several ways that you can take over responsibility for your relative's financial affairs, depending on the state of their physical and mental health. Be aware that their needs may alter rapidly, and be ready to take any necessary steps to increase your level of responsibility before it becomes too late to make changes.

Agent

If the person you care for is mentally capable, but unable to get out, they can still retain overall responsibility for their money but appoint you as their agent. You would be able to cash any pensions and benefits or deal with bank and building society accounts on their behalf. Ask for details at a post office or bank, as many organisations have a standard form.

Powers of attorney

If the person you care for has complicated financial affairs, you may have to consider a **power of attorney**, which is a legal procedure giving you control over their money. The **ordinary** power can be set up for cases where the person is able to give sound instructions; however, it will become invalid if the person becomes mentally incapable. To avoid this problem, most solicitors suggest an **enduring power of attorney** which, after registration, remains valid if your relative becomes too confused to manage their own affairs. It is important that you both take independent advice before setting this up, as it carries a heavy responsibility for the carer that could involve selling property and dealing with taxation. The procedure is very formal so, although not essential, it's usual to set it up through a solicitor. Further information can be obtained from the Public Trust Office (address on p 172).

Court of Protection

If the person you care for is already 'mentally incapable', the action you can take will depend on their income. For state benefits only you can become their **appointee**, a procedure that allows you to manage everything to do with their benefits. If the situation is more complex and you do not already have an enduring power of attorney you can apply to the Court of Protection. They will appoint a receiver (usually a relative) to manage all the financial business. If you do not wish to undertake this duty, a bank or solicitor will act as receiver in your place. Contact the Customer Services Unit of the Public Trust Office (address on p 172).

Managing financial affairs in Scotland

If the **power of attorney** was signed after 1 January 1991, it will remain valid even if the person giving it becomes mentally incapable. A solicitor will be needed to prepare the power of attorney.

If the person you care for has not made a power of attorney and is mentally incapable of looking after their affairs or of appointing someone else to look after them, a **curator bonis** may be required. A curator bonis is a person appointed by and responsible to the Court. This individual – usually, but not necessarily, a solicitor or an accountant – has to manage all the financial affairs and property of the person concerned. Having a curator bonis appointed is expensive, and any professional will charge an annual administration fee. The application to the Court for a curator bonis to be appointed is prepared by a solicitor, usually on behalf of a close relative of the person. For more information contact the Accountant of Court (address on p 163).

Making a will

The person you care for may talk to you about making a will, or they may wish to add to or alter an existing will, if it was made a long time ago and their situation has changed. When someone is ill, they begin to think more about their personal affairs and may ask you to help them sort out the legal arrangements. If you feel uncomfortable or unsure about doing this task, ask someone else to help – perhaps a friend who is sensible and practical but less personally involved. If your relative is unable to go out, many solicitors offer a home service to help people write a will. Look in the Yellow Pages or ask at the Citizens Advice Bureau for details.

Some people draw up their own wills. This is quite in order as long as the correct procedures are followed. The will must be written clearly, and signed and dated in the presence of two (or just one in Scotland) independent witnesses or relatives who are not beneficiaries. The will must name one or more people who are willing to act as executors – the ones responsible for seeing that the instructions written in the will are properly carried out. Executors can be relatives, friends or professional people who provide this service as part of their job (eg an accountant or a solicitor). A person who acts as an executor can also be named in the will as a beneficiary. Information packs and will forms are available from many stationers, and details of other booklets are given below. (If you live in Scotland, make sure that the information covers the law in Scotland.) If your relative's affairs are not simple or straightforward, it would be wise to ask a solicitor to draw up the will; their fees for home and office appointments vary, so telephone and ask for a price guide before booking a home visit.

Why is a will important?

Some people wrongly assume that if their affairs are straightforward they do not need to make a will, because all of their belongings will go directly to their closest relative. But there are strict laws about how a person's estate (the name given to their possessions) is divided up, and it can be complicated and costly to sort out the affairs of someone who has died without making a will (intestate).

The following 'down to earth' comments from a solicitor should help if your relative is undecided and asks your opinion about the benefits of making a will.

- You don't have to have a lot of money to make a will. Making a will is about making sure that your possessions go to the person(s) you want to receive them.
- You mustn't feel morbid about making a will; all you are doing is setting out your plan as to how your assets are to be split up when you die.
- If you do not make a will the rules governing intestacy apply, which may mean that your assets will be given to relatives you do not know or even want to know.
- Just saying to someone that a treasured ornament or a piece of jewellery is theirs when you die is not good enough. The only safe way of making sure that happens is to put it in a will.

Registering a death

A death must be registered in the district where the death occurred, within five days unless the registrar says this period can be extended. (In Scotland, it can be registered in the office for the area where the deceased person normally lived.) Some offices operate an appointment system, so telephone as soon as you receive the Medical Certificate of Cause of Death. In some circumstances the death will be referred to the coroner; if this is the case, you will be advised what to do. It is usual for a relative to register the death but it can be another person.

Two free certificates are given to enable the funeral arrangements to be made but, as many organisations (eg banks and building societies) require a certificate to complete their business, it would be wise to buy extra copies.

For more *i*nformation

i Age Concern Factsheet 7 *Making your will*.

i Age Concern Factsheet 14 *Dealing with someone's estate*.

i Age Concern Factsheet 27 *Arranging a funeral*.

i Age Concern Factsheet 22 *Legal arrangements for managing financial affairs*.

i Age Concern Funeral Planning – a free brochure is available. Tel: 0800 38 77 35

i Age Concern Insurance Services – a range of insurance is available for people over 55.

    – Home Insurance: Tel: 0345 697610
    – Motor Insurance: Tel: 0345 125816
    – Pet Insurance: Tel: 0800 590 229
    – Travel Insurance: 01883 834 887

i Benefits Agency booklet D49 *What to do after a death* is available from DSS offices or local probate registry offices.

i Lord Chancellor's Department booklet PA2 *How to obtain probate* is available from local probate registry offices.

6 Managing stress

Caring for someone who is unwell is stressful for lots of reasons – anxieties about the illness, the extra pressures of caring and the difficulty of managing your own life can all compete with each other to exhaust your mental energies. It's no wonder most carers say that tension rarely sinks far below the surface.

This chapter describes stress in general and helps you to think about some of the personal problems that may be causing your stress. How you deal with difficult situations depends on lots of factors; your personality type, whether you feel in control of the situation and how much energy you have in reserve all play their part in how well you cope.

Everyone needs a few strategies to draw on when the going gets tough. This chapter offers some suggestions to help you build up your personal strengths and support systems, and a selection of coping skills and self-help techniques to use when you need to act calmly and reduce the tension. Learning how to relax your body works wonders when you are feeling over-tired and pressured.

What is stress?

Jane

'I was so uptight I felt as if I would burst.'

The word 'stress' is very popular nowadays and is commonly used to describe the way we feel when pressure is intense. It's not a medical problem but a combination of symptoms produced when our physical, mental and emotional systems go into over-drive. Everyone reacts to stress in the same physical way, whatever the cause or size of the problem, because we are all programmed to behave alike. Unfortunately, though, some people seem to get more upset than others when faced by difficult situations. This more extreme reaction to stress is often a result of their emotional state, their personality type and how well they have learned to cope in the past rather than due to the nature of the problem.

The problems stem from:

- loneliness and isolation;
- shortage of time;
- uncertainty about the future;
- difficult relationships and pressures from other people;
- feeling that life is getting out of control;
- lack of sleep;
- feeling under-valued and over-worked.

Primitive feelings

Joan

'When the pressures built up I wasn't surprised when I found I had raised blood pressure.'

Having to cope with a bit of stress is normal and is important to help people deal with challenges in a positive way, but when there are too many pressures the reaction can be unpleasant. As tension builds up the body goes into over-drive and produces high levels of adrenaline hormone to prepare itself for action in the same way as a primitive caveman who needed to fight or run away from danger ('fight or flight'). Nowadays, though, this type of 'escape' is rarely needed, so, instead of using up the energy generated to deal with the danger (stressful situation), it remains in the body, keeping it in a continual state of tension. While adrenaline levels remain high, the body is constantly in the 'red zone' waiting for the next problem that may lurk around the corner.

When stress becomes distress

A little stress can improve performance: it keeps your brain stimulated and helps you to concentrate and deal with challenging situations. For example, many TV presenters regard a bit of stress as essential: it adds sparkle to their performance and keeps them alert. In everyday terms, you can probably relate this to how you feel as an important event draws near. Your nerves are a bit on edge but your body is designed to deal with the occasional stressful event and after it's over you begin to relax and everything slows down. Unfortunately, if difficult situations happen close together, your body doesn't have sufficient time to recover between the periods of pressure and you begin to feel unwell. The tension can become so intense that you may feel as if you are about to explode and you can no longer handle all of the demands being made of you. Relaxing becomes more difficult as your body tells you that it feels *distressed*.

Mike

'My wife was in hospital, I had to keep my business running and then visit her before I went back to do the paperwork. The thought of the VAT figures filled me with dread.'

Joan

'When my husband was ill and I had my mother to see to as well, I'd have given anything for a day on my own.'

Warning signs

Maureen

' When my mother spilt her tea yet again I saw red. Why couldn't she be more careful. I was late for work, my boss had asked me twice for a report and I had a splitting headache.'

Joan

'To protect my husband I tried to keep life on an even keel, so I took more stress on my own shoulders.'

The typical signs and symptoms that develop when you are feeling over-stressed are triggered by a combination of physical and emotional reactions. Look at the list below and tick the ones that trouble you regularly. If it's more than a few, the time is right to consider some solutions before your own health begins to suffer. The symptoms include:

- headaches;
- feeling tired and listless;
- difficulty in sleeping at either end of the night;
- palpitations and rapid pulse rate;
- indigestion/heartburn;
- breathing problems;
- aching joints;
- over- or under-eating;
- skin problems;
- increased urine output and diarrhoea;
- numbness and pins and needles in limbs;

- poor concentration and difficulty making decisions;
- feeling unhappy and depressed;
- feeling angry, frustrated and helpless;
- feeling irritable and tearful;
- feeling anxious and fearful;
- lost sense of humour.

Where do the stresses come from?

John

'For me the worst part is the tiredness. It makes me irritable and I can't think straight. I long for a break but don't know where to start looking for help. I feel close to collapse.'

Joan

'Peter's illness was always at the back of my mind. When I went out I would always wonder what I might find at home when I returned.'

It is difficult to define stress clearly because it seems to come from two directions, both external and internal. The confusion arises when we talk about stress as a *cause* of problems (pressures from people or situations) or as an *effect* (a response from inside our bodies, such as a tension headache). Both external and internal stresses affect our moods and the physical ability to cope. Unfortunately, not all sources of stress are within our control, and problems can rarely be put into neat little boxes. Mostly we manage to keep the 'lids on the boxes' and give our bodies sufficient rest before dealing with the next set of problems. However, if a string of events happen too close together, pressure builds up to uncomfortable levels and it takes only one small problem to bring everything to a head.

Psychologists refer to these sources of stress as 'life events' and they include major upheavals such as retirement, moving home, changing job, an accident and illness but also lesser events such as Christmas or going on holiday. They aren't particularly special or rare and they aren't necessarily unpleasant, just things that happen to all of us all of the time. Research has shown that, if a combination of events follow hard on each other, without giving the body time to recover, the effects are always worse. The important point to note is that it is the accumulation of both minor and major events that happen close together rather than merely the *severity* of the events.

Linda

'It was hot and my husband was late, which made me feel even more stressed because I dread facing the supermarket to do a big shop when it gets busy.'

If a pattern of events has caused a build-up of tension, it doesn't take much to set nerves jangling. Common predisposing factors are:

- tiredness caused by insufficient sleep or broken sleep patterns such as waking early;
- prolonged pain, perhaps from aching joints or the continual physical strain of moving an ill person;
- strong emotional feelings that stem from anger, sadness or anxiety;
- personality type – some people tend to be more prone to stress than others, particularly if they are impatient by nature;
- pressures created by people or places – relatives, hospital appointments, shopping in crowded supermarkets;
- discomfort caused by lack of fresh air, too much noise or feeling too hot or too cold;
- the weather – some people are affected by too little sunlight;
- things that affect the digestive system – too much alcohol, caffeine in tea and coffee or refined sugar;
- smoking too many cigarettes – stress is the reason many people give for their smoking habit but in the long term it works in reverse because nicotine affects tolerance to stress;

■ changes in life-style that cause uncertainty, such as giving up work, illness or financial worries.

Two personal stories

Jane and Brenda are typical examples of how stress builds up into distress.

Jane

'My husband and I had recently moved house and I felt unsettled and isolated from my friends. My mother suffered a heart attack that caused a great deal of anxiety. I had to travel a long distance to visit her over several weeks and still felt worried after she was settled back at home because I didn't know how well she was taking care of herself. I couldn't sleep because I was uncertain about the future and began to feel unwell with quite a lot of physical and emotional symptoms – bad headaches, extreme tiredness, poor appetite and feelings of panic. The final straw came when someone drove into the back of my car. I felt all alone and didn't know where to turn for help.'

Brenda

'I had been taking care of my father for six months following an operation and I was beginning to feel at the end of my tether. Besides looking after him twice a day, I had a number of other pressures that all seemed to be falling on my shoulders. We were short of staff at work, my boss did not like me having time off to take my father to the hospital and my daughter was pregnant. I was very tempted to start smoking again even though I had given up several years ago. The situation came to a head one day when I burst into tears over a minor event which felt like a mountain. When the situation had calmed down I was left feeling drained, trembling and confused at the strength of my own emotions. Fortunately, a good friend persuaded me I needed to ask for help, so I talked to my GP who arranged for me to see a qualified counsellor in the practice. It helped enormously to talk to someone who listened without passing comments.'

Brenda and Jane had each gone through a difficult period in a short time with a run of problems adding to their stress load. Each story illustrates the kinds of factor that characterise the build-up of pressure:

■ a series of stressful events close together;
■ little control over the individual situations;
■ pressure from other people;
■ little time for your own relaxation.

Brenda is lucky to have had a caring friend who recognised the signs of stress and helped her to find a safety valve by talking to a counsellor. Self-help is also an important way to solve problems, and what people learn about themselves while dealing with a difficult situation increases their ability to cope with future stress. Be aware of early warning signs and learn how to recognise your own body signals so that you can reduce the pressure before it builds to uncomfortable levels. However, there are no magic potions – stress management, like any other skill, needs to be learned and practised.

Getting the balance right

The key to managing stress is getting the balancing act right between tension and relaxation – like a juggler, if you get too many balls in the air at once they all come bouncing down. Balancing the needs of your relative against your own needs may not be easy. Caring brings extra responsibilities and you may be the main person they rely on. Unfortunately, you are the one most likely to end up with too much stress and too little time for relaxation. Tension and anxiety can't be switched off to order but this does not mean they should be ignored. There are ways to ease the pressure and give your body a rest, and stress is easier to bear if you understand where the problems are coming from and you feel that you have some control over how the situation is managed.

Iris

'I divide the day into three parts – morning, afternoon and evening. I take each part at a time and have learned to be flexible, to manage what I can.'

Joan

'When it stopped, I looked back and wondered how I coped – I know that I tried to keep my home and work separate.'

Stress diary

Keeping a stress diary can help to sort out where some of the pressure is coming from. Start the process by making a list of all the things that have bothered you in the last week. Next jot down by the side of each problem how you felt at the time – angry, anxious, irritable etc. Now cross out things that you chose to do – they may have been difficult, but if you entered into a situation willingly you were less likely to be upset by the effort. Look at the remainder of the problems on your list and ask yourself if they could be the fundamental causes of your anxiety. The reason why many people get angry and upset about some situations and not others is usually linked to their feelings about choice. It's far easier to deal with a problem if you know that you have some control over the event.

Gill

'My husband is ill and needs care. I want to look after him at home for as long as I am able, however difficult. We are very close and I want him at home with me.'

If Gill's decision to care for her husband resulted from external pressures – for example, from other family members – she would be more likely to feel resentful because demands were being placed on her with little opportunity to say 'no'. However, because she has made a personal decision to care for her husband she feels calm about the outcome.

125

Mental stimulation

Harry

'I wanted to be at home to take care of my wife after her operation, so the decision to take early retirement was mine, but I did miss the stimulation of the office. I felt much better when I started an evening class at the local college. A neighbour stays with my wife and I am now learning about local history.'

Stress doesn't always arise from intense activity. It's also possible to feel frustrated and unsettled if you are bored. Challenges keep the body and brain stimulated, so being isolated at home or doing the same repetitive jobs day after day can be equally distressful.

It is unrealistic to attempt to choose or control every aspect of your life, but try to maintain a balance between the challenging bits and the relative calm. For example, if time at home is pressured, don't take on extra responsibilities outside the house and make the most of respite opportunities by doing something pleasant and relaxing – it's not the time to take an adventure holiday.

Helping yourself

There are two ways that people commonly deal with stress. The first is a form of self-defence in which they justify something that they know is not true but convince themselves that in the short term it may do some good. They tell themselves that their actions are for the best in the hope that the situation will improve without too much effort. A person who smokes may say 'my smoking helps to reduce my stress' when in truth they know that this is not the case. Unfortunately, pretending only masks problems; it never cures them and they continue to niggle away in the background.

The other way of dealing with stress is much more positive because it focuses on doing something for yourself and puts you back in charge. This form of self-help encourages you to face problems squarely and find ways to change or adapt situations.

There will still be problems, because it is impossible to achieve a stress-free life, but in this way you lessen the effects.

Learning to cope with pressure

By now you've probably got a clearer picture about the main causes of your stress and feel ready to make some changes that will help you to cope. Start the process by asking yourself the following questions to identify your strong points:

- How have I dealt with difficult situations in the past?
- What lessons did I learn?
- What's different this time round?
- Who (or what) can I turn to for support?
- Will the problem go away if I don't deal with it?
- Would talking to someone else help?
- Are the problems as bad as I think or has anxiety clouded my common sense?
- What sorts of change do I need to make to help me get along?

Finding long-term solutions

No one ever cured their stress overnight, so don't rush into hasty decisions. Look at each problem separately with four courses of action in mind:

1 Is it necessary to change the situation? This may call for major action, such as your relative moving into a nursing home. Making a decision of this nature will be extremely upsetting so don't attempt to do it alone. But if you are finding it very difficult to cope, it could be the right long-term solution.
2 Can you improve your ability to deal with the situation? Your stress levels might fall quite dramatically if you ease some of the pressure on yourself and your time. A practical solution, such as getting help with the housework, could be the answer.
3 Do you need to change your perception of the situation? Ask yourself if the problem is as bad as you think it is and try to

turn some of the threats into challenges. Positive 'self-talk' works well here: tell yourself that you have dealt with difficult situations before and that you have ample reserves of inner strength.

4 Would changing your behaviour help? Doing things through habit is easy, especially if you are feeling upset, but you may have slipped into patterns of behaviour that increase your stress. If you are rushing around frantically, slow down so that your actions become calmer. This gives your brain a less stressed message. Cut down on the amount of coffee and tea you drink; the caffeine they contain stimulates the nervous system, causing irritability and insomnia. Change any routines that are particularly tiring; for example, avoid shopping at the supermarket when you know it will be busy.

Jean

'I take help now, especially with practical things. My husband used to do all the practical jobs, but I am happy that my neighbour will cut the lawn or drive us to the hospital clinic.'

Joan

'Look ahead and prepare yourself. It's easier to deal with problems and keeps your mind at rest if you have a plan worked out.'

Personal resources

Ann

'My husband is older than me and he's not so active now. I felt concerned about leaving him, but I have to get out sometimes or I wouldn't be able to carry on. I went to see a counsellor and she helped me draw up a list of my main strengths and encouraged me to draw on the support of people I trust. It was very reassuring to think about all of my personal resources: I have:

- firm relationships with husband, children, family and friends;
- good physical health;
- a positive mental attitude – I feel confident and good about myself;
- a sense of humour;
- financial security;
- spiritual support;
- no dependence on smoking, alcohol or drugs.

The counsellor also encouraged me to think about where I could help myself further. I could improve my ability to cope by:

- finding more time for myself and having a relaxing hobby;
- learning to say 'no' sometimes;
- cutting back on some of the household jobs that are not a high priority.'

Like Ann, you can also identify your strengths and think about where you feel vulnerable. Then talk to someone you trust about what steps you could take to improve the areas where you feel insecure, at least to the point where you feel less anxious.

Brenda

'I've learned not to keep it all bottled up, and I meet with friends regularly. We rarely talk about my worries, but I know I can when I need to, and it helps.'

Joan

'It never crossed my mind that I could ask for counselling. I had enormous help from my sons but I never thought about asking anyone else.'

Finding support

Any support is valuable when you are feeling under pressure, especially the undemanding type that comes from family and friends. Asking for help is not a sign of weakness; it's more an awareness that problems can seldom be solved in isolation. If you need to talk to someone, ask for a listening ear, as friends and relatives may be reluctant to interfere unless they are invited. Once you have given the signal that help would be welcome, you should discuss with the other person how this can be achieved without upsetting your relationship. It's important to agree a few basic rules at the beginning, because the last thing you want is someone marching in and taking over. For example, the person you talk to must respect your need for confidentiality; you may become emotional and let off a 'bit of steam'; and you must feel free to ignore their advice without giving offence.

If talking to a friend or relative is not the best course for you because you would find this uncomfortable or there isn't a suitable person, other options are available:

- self-help and carers' groups run by social services, health trusts or at a carers' centre;
- private counsellors (ask at your GP practice or the Citizens Advice Bureau for a list of professional counsellors who are trained and registered);
- religious leaders;
- telephone helplines (eg CarersLine 0345 573 369 run by Carers National Association);
- Samaritans (national 24-hour helpline staffed by trained counsellors who offer emotional support to people who are feeling isolated and in despair – 08457 909090 or see the local telephone directory).

Breathing habits

Breathing is an unconscious action that you rarely think about, but over the years you may have developed poor breathing habits without realising their significance. When your body is calm, breathing is slow, regular and deep. Your rib cage and diaphragm expand, drawing air into the lungs, which expand to fill the whole of the chest cavity, and the abdomen swells; then the rib cage and diaphragm contract, forcing the air out of the lungs.

When anxiety levels are high, breathing becomes fast, irregular and shallow, and air enters only the top part of the chest cavity. Fast breathing is a natural body defence set off by the primitive force that helps you respond to danger. It enables your body to exchange oxygen and carbon dioxide rapidly. Unfortunately, prolonged anxiety creates a state where the body is continually on 'red alert'. Oxygen is inhaled and carbon dioxide exhaled in excess of your actual needs, leading to an imbalance of gases in your blood stream. This type of breathing – known as hyperventilation or over-breathing – is quite common; if it remains unchecked, breathing patterns change, leading to breath-holding and deep sighing.

These irregular breathing patterns are part of a cycle that is self-triggering. Increased anxiety sends messages to the brain to prepare it for action: the body goes into panic mode and the fear reactions start up; over-breathing leads to too much oxygen in the system and causes symptoms of dizziness, faintness and tingling in the face and limbs; these feelings are frightening and the brain receives another false message triggered by the fear, and so the process continues. People who have become 'chronic hyperventilators' often experience a long list of physical symptoms that mimic more serious medical conditions, such as chest pains, numbness, muscle spasm and even collapse. Hyperventilation is not a serious condition and can be corrected by practising correct breathing exercises. If you have felt any chest pains, talk to your doctor first, who may be able to recommend someone to help you with breathing therapy.

Ann

'I found that the breathing methods taught at the relaxation group changed the way I felt, and then I became more in control generally.'

Better breathing

Although breathing is normally controlled by the 'involuntary nervous system', it's possible to take control of the process and calm the system down when feelings of panic begin to rise. People who learn to correct poor breathing habits soon notice an improvement in their anxiety state. The following guidelines will help remedy over-breathing and generally reduce tension:

- As soon as anxiety levels begin to rise, quietly tell yourself to 'calm down'. This sends a positive message to the brain.
- Slow down all your movements, because rushing around increases agitation and your body responds by producing more adrenaline to deal with the 'threat'.
- Calm your breathing deliberately and keep an even rhythm with a slight pause between the in and out breaths; imagine a candle in front of your face that flickers gently as you breathe out.
- Practise calm breathing at different times during the day so that you are aware of the feeling of taking control; it's much easier to recognise the correct pattern when you are not over-anxious.
- Feel how you breathe by placing one hand on your abdomen and the other on your upper chest – as you breathe in, the lower hand should rise first.
- If you think that you hyperventilate, get a friend to count your breathing when you are unaware: 10–12 breaths per minute is average. Over-breathers regularly breathe at 15–20 breaths per minute and can reach 30 breaths per minute when feeling very frightened.
- If you feel faint or dizzy with pins and needles in your limbs as a result of breathing too shallowly, quietly cup your hands over your nose and breathe in and out into your hands. By inhaling carbon dioxide you will swiftly restore the balance of chemicals in the blood stream. Some doctors recommend a paper bag for this restoring action but that can be rather obvious, whereas people will take little notice of your hands.
- Avoid wearing tight clothing that constricts your abdomen and restricts your breathing. Let your stomach muscles relax even if it does make you look fatter; women are conditioned to holding in their stomachs to create a better body outline but this interferes with deep breathing.

Decreasing the tension

Ann

'The counsellor suggested a relaxation group. I was reluctant at first, but I found that, although it didn't change the fact that my husband is ill, I coped better with it all.'

If your body is already feeling tired and strained, any movements that increase muscular tension are an extra drain on your energy reserves. So it's worth being as relaxed as possible in all of your movements. Ask a friend to observe your general posture or catch sight of yourself in the mirror or a shop window. Look out for uncomfortable positions and bad habits:

- head thrusting forward or down with your chin hard on your chest;
- shoulders hunched and rounded;
- arms held tightly across your chest or stiffly by your sides with hands clenched;
- legs crossed and twined together;
- restless habits such as tapping your fingers and feet, or hair twisting;
- nail biting and teeth clenching.

Learning to relax

Deep relaxation is an excellent way to restore energy and boost your spirit but it does need time and space. Merely telling yourself to relax rarely works, especially if you are feeling overwrought. Relaxation requires practice and it helps if you understand how the technique works. It's all about fooling the system and giving out positive signals that your body is at ease. Relaxed muscles send calm messages to the brain in a similar way that control of breathing turns off the false reaction to danger. When there are no threats, your body rests and restores itself ready for the next burst of energy.

Whole body relaxation

This is the most common form of relaxation and produces pleasant results quickly. It's a skill that is easy to learn but, just as you didn't learn to walk in a day, you won't learn to relax in one session. The technique always works if you create the right conditions and allow sufficient time – about 20 minutes for a whole body session. Eventually, you can cut down on the time and recreate the stress-free feeling anywhere as you improve your skill. If you would like to learn to relax with a teacher, ask at your GP surgery; many stress counsellors run individual or group classes.

Step-by-step technique for use at home

1 Find a warm, quiet place and lie on a rug or sit in a well sup-ported chair. Use a pillow for support if it makes you more comfortable. Reduce outside noises if possible.

2 Wear loose clothing and remove glasses and shoes. Lie on your back or sit upright in a chair with head supported, arms and legs straight and slightly apart.

3 Breathe in and out deeply for three breaths and imagine you are losing tension; then breathe normally.

4 You can close your eyes at this stage or wait until they shut naturally. You are going to work on each major muscle group, starting with the feet. (As you tighten and relax the muscles, learn to recognise the difference between tension and relax-ation. Hold each constriction for a few seconds and repeat each action with a short break between.)

5 Pull your feet towards your body – hold the tension – release and feel the reduction in tension.

6 Point your toes hard away from your body and feel the tension in your calf muscles – hold – and relax.

7 Next work on your thighs by drawing your legs tightly towards you, knees pointing upwards – hold – drop back to a relaxed position with feet, lower legs and thighs rolled outwards.

8 Tense your buttocks by squeezing them together hard – hold – and relax.

9 Tense your abdomen in the opposite way by pushing it outwards – hold – and then let it flop.

10 Check your legs again and if you have slipped back into a tense position have a second go from step 5. A couple of deep breaths will help at this point. Your lower body should feel heavy, warm and relaxed.

11 Now concentrate on your back. Arch your spine away from the floor or chair – hold – and let go. (***Warning*** Leave this one out if you have any back problems.)

12 Now move your shoulders backwards to expand your chest – hold – and relax.

13 Tense your shoulders next by raising your arms and pulling on your shoulders – hold – as you drop your arms, wriggle your shoulders up to your ears – relax with your shoulder blades touching the floor or chair.

14 Now work on your hands and lower arms by making a tight fist – hold – and relax, letting your fingers droop. As you clench your fists for the second time, raise your arms slightly and notice the tension in your forearms – hold – and relax.

15 Move to the upper arms by bringing your hands across your body, close to your chest – hold – relax them to a position on the floor or on your thighs with palms facing upwards.

16 Relax your neck and throat by gently moving your head from side to side (not a circular movement) and then pulling your chin down to your chest – hold – and relax.

17 Next clench your jaw by clamping your teeth together – hold – and let go so that your mouth is slightly open. That tension probably felt familiar, as clenching teeth is a common habit.

18 Now work on your facial muscles. Press your lips together – hold – and relax. Push your tongue hard to the roof of your mouth – hold – and let it drop to the floor of your mouth.

19 Move your eyes inside your closed lids to the four quarters of a circle and then let your eyelids relax.

20 Finally, relax your forehead and scalp. Frown hard and pull your forehead down – hold – and let go so that your face feels floppy.

Your whole body should now feel comfortable and free from tension. Breathe gently and let your mind wander at will. If stressful thoughts irritate you in this relaxed state, think about somewhere pleasant and, as you breathe, repeat in your mind 'peace in and pressure out'. Don't worry if you drop off at this point; eventually you will learn to relax your body without going to sleep, but use this method at night if insomnia is a problem.

Lie quietly with your eyes closed for a few minutes, enjoying the warm feeling; then slowly bring yourself back to the present. Count backwards from five to one, clench your fists tightly, relax and rub your hands together. If you are lying on the floor, roll onto your side; open your eyes with your hands shielding them from the light. Stand up slowly and try to hold on to the relaxed mood when you return to action.

Getting the best from relaxation

Sharing the session with another person is pleasant. You can take turns to read the instructions or make yourselves a tape recording. Listen to music if it helps to calm your mind, and ring the changes by starting at your head and working towards your feet. As you become better at 'switching off', shorten the session and create a relaxed mood by imagining your body is warm and heavy without going through all of the muscle-tightening steps. Use this shortened version as a mini-restorative, particularly when you are away from home in stressful situations – and begin to enjoy your new, confident self.

Fact Box

Comments from a stress counsellor

- ▪ Negative thought patterns can make an illness worse.
- ▪ Social support from family and friends can help to alleviate stress.
- ▪ Relaxation offsets the effects of too much stress.
- ▪ 'Coping' habits such as smoking, drinking and over- or under-eating make things worse.
- ▪ Illness can be an opportunity to improve one's life-style.

Conclusion

Stress is normal in small doses and harmful when it becomes so severe that it feels *distressful*. The warning signs are common to everyone, but some people – perhaps because of personality type or bad past experiences – react to pressure more quickly than others. The key to managing stress is learning to recognise where your pressures are coming from and decide whether you have a choice about changing the situation or accepting that some situations cannot be controlled. When your body gives off the tell-tale signals that tension is rising, try to calm yourself by slowing your movements, breathing quietly and evenly, and relaxing your muscles. Let your shoulders drop, and unwind all the parts of your body that have become 'twisted' together. Use your support systems and don't feel it's a weakness to ask for help or show signs of emotion. Crying or allowing yourself to tremble are good ways to relieve tension.

The next chapter looks at some complementary treatments that are excellent ways of relieving tension and giving yourself a treat.

For more *i*nformation

- ❶ The British Association for Counselling publishes a directory of counsellors in the UK (address on p 164).

- ❶ The 'Family Doctor' series booklet *Understanding Stress* is available from most pharmacist/chemist shops.

- ❶ Music tapes: *The Fairy Ring & Silver Wings* by Mike Rowland and *Spirit of the Rainforest* by Terry Oldfield are soothing tapes to use for relaxation. Available from music shops or by catalogue from New World Aurora (address on p 172).

- ❶ The Relaxation for Living Trust publishes a wide range of materials to help reduce stress: leaflets, audio tapes, books and a newsletter (address on p 173).

- ❶ The Royal College of Psychiatrists publishes a range of leaflets for dealing with anxieties, phobias, depression, bereavement and other difficulties (address on p 173).

7 Complementary treatments to help with stress

We live in a world that is so fast and furious, even our most recent ancestors would probably find it difficult to recognise. Few of us are able to escape the pressures, demands and problems that seem always to be increasing, and 'stress' is a word on everybody's lips: stress and stress-related problems cost the NHS millions of pounds a year in treatment. However, as hermit-like seclusion isn't really a practical option, we need to find other more agreeable ways to protect ourselves from the traumas of modern living.

This chapter helps to do that by looking at some of the therapies and treatments that can be used alongside orthodox medicine to treat stress and give a boost to body and spirit. It describes some of the popular complementary treatments such as aromatherapy, reflexology, homoeopathy and meditation, and suggests how you and your relative might benefit. Some can easily be practised at home using basic remedies and techniques but for others it would be advisable to see a qualified practitioner.

The terms 'alternative therapy' and 'complementary treatment' are used to describe a range of treatments available from practitioners and therapists who work alongside doctors in conventional medicine. Most of these methods aim to treat the whole body and are intended to complement, rather than replace, orthodox medicine.

All complementary treatments can be obtained without going to a medically trained doctor but this does not mean that an NHS or private doctor will not or cannot provide some alternative treatments; some doctors are dually trained and, increasingly, some GPs are recommending the benefits of such therapies. Not all therapies are widely available in the UK; ask at your local library or GP practice.

Florence

'My daughter encouraged me to have a weekly treat while my husband was at his physiotherapy session, so I went to an aromatherapist – it was wonderful. My daughter took me the first time because I was nervous but I need not have been, the aromatherapist made me feel special.'

Many popular alternative treatments originated in the East and have been practised there for centuries. They rely on ancient knowledge linked to herbal remedies and traditional practices that are believed to stimulate the body's own healing powers; acupuncture from China and yoga from India are obvious examples. Some of the newer therapies appeal more to Western scientific minds and are gaining in popularity as aids to diagnosis as well as treatment by practitioners of alternative therapies. Two examples are colour therapy, which draws links between certain colours and mental harmony or stress, and iridology, which examines the eyes for clues to hidden disorders.

Many of these treatments are still thought by some to verge on quackery and the people who practise them to be cranks. But this view is changing and information can easily be found in books and magazine articles; products are displayed on supermarket shelves and complementary treatments are sometimes offered through the NHS. The change in thinking has come about in several ways: people have more open minds and are encouraged to practise self-help; they feel more confident about using an increasing range of 'over-the-counter' remedies; and there are attractive 'natural' herb-based products readily available in high street stores that have demystified the image of harmful magic potions.

However, an element of caution must always be exercised when buying and using products that have been purchased over the counter (ie without a prescription). Many contain poisonous ingredients that could be harmful if the dosage is exceeded. Be sure to follow the instructions carefully, and ask your own or your relative's doctor whether the product might have an adverse effect.

Finding a qualified therapist

A word of caution here: any book, however specialist, can give only limited information and can never be a substitute for the advice and treatment provided by experienced, qualified practitioners. Ask for details of reputable, local therapists at your surgery or health centre or contact the national organisations listed in the sections 'For more information'. Word of mouth can be a good form of recommendation but do make sure any therapist you visit is registered to practise with the appropriate national body.

Don't be embarrassed to ask directly about qualifications, as all trained therapists will be pleased to offer reassurance and tell you how to check. Properly trained therapists take a full medical history before prescribing and have learned about the dosage and combinations of herbs, whereas untrained people can only guess and may do harm. There are some ready-made treatments available in health shops, but, before taking any over-the-counter medication, it would be wise to go to the doctor first, so as not to delay diagnosis or effective orthodox treatment. Finally, whichever alternative treatment you choose, it's wise to consult a medical doctor if symptoms persist.

Aromatherapy

Julia, an aromatherapist

'Aromatherapy may be used to induce a deep sense of relaxation and well-being, combating the negative effects of stress and anxiety.'

The ancient art of aromatherapy combines the restorative properties of aromatic plant essences with massage and is an excellent therapy to try if complementary treatments are new to you and your relative. Its gentle methods encourage reduction of stress, and a trained therapist will ask questions first to discover the best treatment for each individual person. The complex essential oils extracted from many plants are introduced into body where the 'life force' of the plant's essential oil can have a curative effect. Therapists do not claim that the oils heal directly in the sense that a synthetic drug may effect a cure; instead it is believed that the oils encourage the body to use its own natural healing forces from within. The essential oils are absorbed through the skin and pass through the tissues to the blood stream and so travel around the body. Different oil combinations affect different parts of the body, for example, camomile can help with digestive problems.

Selecting oils

Julia, an aromatherapist

'When buying aromatherapy oils, always choose 'pure essential' oils to ensure good quality. Labels that state 'fragrance' or 'blend' are synthetic and are useful only as mood creators or to scent a room. There are recognised retail outlets in most high streets – try good health food, bodycare and herbalist shops and the larger supermarkets.'

Essential oils are extracted from plant essences by a special distillation process that changes their chemical composition. They are used in concentrations that are many times stronger than their original plant form, each individual plant holding only very small quantities of oil. Rose oil is the most expensive to purchase because it takes 20 rose heads to obtain one drop of essential oil.

Essential oils are rarely used undiluted, because they are too powerful to use directly on the skin (and some might be dangerous in pregnancy). They are diluted with a good quality, unrefined or cold-pressed vegetable oil such as peach or almond oil, which also acts as a lubricant to allow the hands to move freely over the skin. (A refined oil may have been subjected to chemical processing.) To start a basic collection it is advisable to choose about six key oils from the aroma 'families': spicy, earthy, floral, citrus, herbal, pine-like and woody are good examples. You can then select and mix oils according to your mood at the time of massage. To practise aromatherapy effectively you will need to read about the oils in more depth and learn how to massage them into the skin. The following list gives examples of the essential oils an aromatherapist would use.

- For *nervous tension* and *anxiety* use cypress, frankincense, sweet marjoram, petitgrain, rose otto, vetiver, ylang-ylang.
- As an *anti-depressant* use grapefruit, lavender, neroli or orange blossom, orange, patchouli.
- For *stimulation* use basil, black pepper, coriander, peppermint, rosemary.
- As a *balancer* to *relax* or *stimulate* use bergamot, geranium.
- To *reduce pain* use bergamot, lavender.
- To *ease coughing* use lavender, sandalwood.

It is important to be aware of the potency of essential oils and that their use is not advised with people who suffer from certain conditions – in particular, a history of miscarriage, haemophilia or advanced varicose veins, and during a high temperature. Always read the instructions carefully before use or follow the advice of a therapist. Oils should **never** be taken by mouth unless prescribed by a medically qualified doctor.

Methods for use at home

> ### *Julia,* an aromatherapist
>
> 'At the end of a day, try a ten-minute, luxuriant aromatherapy bath, using two drops each of lavender, sandalwood and ylang-ylang pure essential oils, to promote a peaceful and restful night's sleep.'

The soothing oils can be used in other ways to enhance their effect.

- **Vaporisation** creates a very pleasant effect by burning oils in special containers, so that the aroma is inhaled from the air. It is believed that the healing part of the oil is breathed into the body and passes through the membranes of the lungs into the blood system. Fill the bowl with water, add two to four drops of essential oil and place a lighted night-light candle underneath. Pottery containers and blended oils are readily available in many gift shops.
- **Oils** blended with other creams give extra benefit in skin care to reduce dry skin and enrich hand creams.
- **Hand/foot baths** with five drops of blended oils added to the water relax the body or ease aching joints.
- Use in **steam inhalers** or **droplets on a handkerchief** to bring relief from colds and catarrh.
- Use as **room fresheners** by mixing two drops of essential oil in a cup of cool, boiled water and spray the air using a plant sprayer; or mix a few drops of blended oil with *pot-pourri* or put a few droplets onto a cloth and lay it on a radiator.

Aromatherapy massage

This treatment has little in common with the traditional Swedish massage, which is much more vigorous. The secret of aromatherapy lies in the skill of the therapist choosing the right essential oil to suit the mood of the person and help their specific problem. Oils are chosen from three main groups in order to invigorate the body and improve mental well-being, to help tone and regulate the body functions, and to create a feeling of calm.

For more *i*nformation

ⓘ To obtain a list of qualified practitioners in your area, contact one of the following organisations (addresses in the 'Useful addresses' section):

– Aromatherapy Organisation Council;
– International Federation of Aromatherapists;
– International Society of Professional Aromatherapists;
– Register for Qualified Aromatherapists.

ⓘ *Practical Aromatherapy*, 2nd edn, by S Price, published by Thorsons.

ⓘ *Aromatherapy A–Z* by P Davies, published by CW Daniel Co.

Basic massage

Eddy

'I wasn't sure at first when my wife said "Let me give you a massage" but she had bought some special oils and I felt so much more relaxed after she had finished.'

Therapeutic touch, particularly from Eastern cultures, has always been associated with helping to heal people who are sick and distressed. Massage is now much more widely accepted in Western society and is used by sports people and as a complement to everyday medicine. As a quick energiser, stimulator or salve for aching muscles there is no better treatment. If you feel tired or have a tension headache, it is easy to self-massage using the forehead and neck versions outlined below. Vaporise an essential oil in the room and use soft music to increase the feeling of relaxation and create the right atmosphere.

Jo

'I was offered a simple massage in my private hospital. It was only my shoulders and arms, not my whole body as that would have been too tiring after my operation. I felt really good.'

Simple massage is excellent for reducing muscular tension, because it triggers several body actions: it stimulates the circulation, eases painful muscles and generally creates a feeling of pleasure. Unfortunately, the term 'massage' can conjure up visions of disreputable 'parlours' from the back streets of the world. The massage described here is intended only as a method of relieving stress that can be done by a professional therapist or performed at home. Touch is one of our earliest forms of communication, so use it as a way of helping someone else. Some people find it difficult to touch another person in a non-relationship, non-professional situation, but this form of stress-relieving massage can be used very effectively with relatives and friends.

Giving a massage

Phyllis

'I got a book from the library and read about massage and was so curious about its claims that I treated myself to the real thing. I know enough now to help my husband and family when they are feeling a bit uptight.'

Giving a basic massage requires little training and you cannot do any harm because you are not interfering with body systems in an intrusive sense. Look upon it as a stroking action that soothes the skin and eases tense muscles. Traditional or Swedish massage uses three main actions: stroking, kneading and striking. The first two are the most useful movements for untrained people to use at home. The best places to start are the shoulders, arms and forehead. That way you can provide relief from tension without either of you feeling uncomfortable or embarrassed.

Before you start

There are a few general rules you and your relative should follow that will help achieve the greatest benefit from the massage.

■ Choose appropriate surroundings and get into comfortable positions, warm and free from external interruptions – a chair in the lounge is fine.

- Remove your jewellery and make sure your fingernails are short.
- Both of you need to spend a few minutes relaxing before the massage starts, because tension from the giver can transmit to the receiver.
- Warm your hands and rest them on your relative for a short while, to set up contact.
- Choose a pleasant-smelling oil and put it in a warm dish nearby so that you can dip one hand into it without changing the rhythm. You should give firm, even strokes, applying pressure without hurting (forget pictures of greasy, body-pummelling masseurs!). Keep contact with the skin throughout, because the massage should feel like a continuous flowing movement.
- Change the pressure in different areas of the body (ie light over the bony parts and stronger over the muscle). Most people are not firm enough when they first start to massage. Let your relative tell you what feels good.
- Avoid heavy pressure directly over the spine.
- The areas around the upper trunk are most prone to tension: shoulders, arms, neck and forehead.
- Your relative should spend about 20 minutes resting after the massage to maximise the feeling.

Muscle tension

If your relative is particularly tense, you will feel areas of lumpy, 'knotted' muscle. Pay special attention to these taut places by kneading with your thumbs and the heels of your palms and smoothing the surrounding areas. These areas may be tender, so take care and listen to your relative's reactions.

Forehead

1 Your relative sits in a comfortable upright chair with you standing behind.
2 Warm your hands by rubbing them together and lightly coat them with an unrefined base oil or an aromatherapy oil mixture.
3 Place both hands on the centre of your relative's forehead, with fingertips touching, and then use firm, sweeping strokes,

repeating several times. Keep the movement continuous by replacing one hand with the other.

4   Move your hands in two directions: first sweep upwards towards the hairline and then downwards towards the cheek bones.

5   Finish by resting your hands for a few seconds. Ask your relative how they feel, because it is important for both of you that the massage feels right. Your relative will feel relieved and uplifted, and you will probably feel equally soothed.

Neck and shoulders

Method one

1   Your relative sits in a comfortable chair with you standing behind. Clip or tie back long hair if necessary.

2   Apply an oil if you are going to use your hands on bare skin, but the massage can be done over clothing with good effect.

3   Place your hands on your relative's neck, just below the ears, with fingers touching; in a continuous movement, sweep your hands across the shoulders and stop at the tops of the arms.

4   Repeat several times.

5   Finish by resting your hands for a few seconds. Your relative should feel that tension in the neck and shoulders has been swept away.

Method two

1   Your positions are as for method one, but start with your hands at the neck end of the shoulders, palms cupped over the muscle.

2   Keeping your hands in contact with the shoulders, use the flat part of your thumbs to knead (circular pressure) the area at the back of the neck in as wide a sweep as the thumbs can reach. Do **not** place pressure directly over the spine.

3   Do this as long as your relative feels comfortable. (This area can become very knotty with tension and is a good place to self-massage.)

4   If your relative has a tension headache, knead more up towards the base of the skull.

Arms

1   Prepare as before and place your relative's arm on a protective towel, palm facing down.
2   Put both of your hands on the back of their *lower* arm and, using a firm movement, glide both hands up to the elbow.
3   Separate your hands and slide them down again, gripping round the arm, and off the end of the hand.
4   Using both hands, knead the back of the forearm, working from wrist to elbow.
5   Repeat the sequence on the upper arm.
6   Next massage the elbow with a circular movement. Use plenty of oil, because this area can be dry and becomes sore if the elbows are regularly rested in bed or on chair arms.
7   Ask your relative to raise their forearm and, using your thumbs, knead the front of the forearm from wrist to elbow. Repeat several times.
8   Finish the arm massage by lightly stroking (feathering movement) from the top of the arm to the fingertips. Repeat several times and then do the other arm.
9   If your relative finds that your massaging the whole arm is tiring, try massaging just the lower arms and hands.

For more *i*nformation

🛈   To obtain a list of qualified practitioners of therapeutic massage, contact the UK College for Complementary Health Care Studies (address on p 175).

🛈   *The Complete Guide to Massage* by Susan Mumford, published by Hamlyn.

🛈   *Pocket Massage for Stress Relief* by Clare Maxwell-Hudson, published by Dorling Kindersley.

Acupressure

Acupressure is an ancient skill practised in China and Japan for over 3,000 years. It combines massage with the principles of acupuncture (without using needles), and is thought to have been the forerunner of acupuncture. Acupressure is believed to improve the body's healing powers, prevent illness and promote energy. Practitioners work on known pressure points with thumbs, finger tips, palms, elbows, knees and feet to balance the flow of energy called 'chi', which runs through 'meridians' or invisible channels throughout the body. Acupressure relieves the symptoms of many conditions and is best used in conjunction with other natural or orthodox treatments. It is thought to be beneficial with many stress-induced conditions: allergies, asthma, back pain, depression, insomnia, migraine and general tension.

Therapists are widely available. Each will take a full personal history and then use acupressure points to sedate or stimulate the energy channels. Weekly treatments may be needed to improve a problem, or your relative could just enjoy a regular tone-up to promote well-being. Instructions for 'self-help' acupressure can be taken from a book and practised on yourself or with a partner; however, it is advisable that only minor everyday problems such as headache or common digestive conditions are treated without the expertise of a trained practitioner. A useful technique to try will help relieve nausea caused by travel sickness or anxiety. This remedy is supported by research at Belfast University's Department of Anaesthesia that has shown that the use of pressure bands (sea bands) worn around the wrists does ease feelings of nausea.

Method

1   Press with the pad of your thumb on the point called 'pericardium 6', about 5cm (2 inches) from the wrist between the tendons. The pressure should be firm enough to cause some discomfort but not pain.
2   Hold for 5–10 minutes. Repeat as often as necessary.

For more *i*nformation

ⓘ To find your nearest practitioner, contact the Shen Tao Foundation (address on p 174) enclosing an sae.

ⓘ *Acupressure for Health, Vitality and First Aid Health Essentials* by Jon Sandifer, published by Element Books.

Bach flower remedies

These remedies are named after the medical and homoeopathic trained doctor who researched the healing power of plants in the 1930s. He believed that the characteristics of disorders, whether physical or psychological, could be treated by a cure drawn from plants, sunlight, spring water and fresh air. In practice the remedies tend to be used to treat symptoms that stem from conditions with a psychological basis. This does not imply that the conditions are imagined, simply that they stem from whole body experiences that affect the mind as well as the body. Good examples are the conditions that cause people to feel worried, depressed, exhausted, irritable and panicky.

People have always made use of medicinal herbs, but the 38 Bach remedies claim to use the essential energy within the plant rather than actual plant material. This healing energy is stored in a preserving liquid that can be bought in a concentrated form known as the *stock remedy*. The concentrated forms are then diluted by mixing with pure water and an alcohol preservative. It's usual to combine several concentrates to form the required final treatment. Because the action of Bach remedies is mild, they cannot result in unpleasant reactions or side effects, and can be used with all age groups and animals. Although orthodox medicine cannot offer a sound reason for their claimed effects, practitioners believe that, by looking at psychological symptoms, people are encouraged to review other aspects of their behaviour, life-style and attitudes, and this self-awareness contributes towards the healing process.

Bach remedies are available at many health shops and through specially trained therapists. They are intended primarily as a self-help form of treatment and it is therefore very easy to understand and prepare the remedies using books. The following list gives suggestions about how the remedies can be used; to treat yourself you need to read about them in more depth:

- For exhaustion and feeling drained of energy by long-standing problems, use olive.
- For the after-effects of accident, shock, fright and grief, use star of Bethlehem.
- For apprehension for no known reason, use aspen.
- For tension, fear, and uncontrolled and irrational thoughts, use cherry plum.

Rescue remedy

Five of the remedies – cherry plum, clematis, impatiens, rock rose and star of Bethlehem – were combined by Dr Bach into an emergency treatment he called Rescue Remedy. It can be used for a number of problems associated with shock and injury to help create a calm, soothing feeling. It can be bought as liquid or cream preparations for internal or external treatment and can be used on cuts, bites or after a traumatic experience.

For more *i*nformation

i To find your nearest trained practitioner and details of publications, tapes and educational material, contact the Bach Centre (address on p 164).

i A comprehensive book list, including *The Twelve Healers & Other Remedies* by Edward Bach, can be obtained from CW Daniel Co Ltd, 1 Church Path, Saffron Walden, Essex CB10 1JP, or the Bach Centre (address on p 164).

Homoeopathy

Homoeopathy uses minute amounts of natural substances to enhance the body's own healing power. The practice is centuries old and is widely used as the sole form of treatment or as a complement to orthodox medicine. Practitioners are trained in homoeopathic medicine and many also have a general medical qualification. The name 'homoeopathy' is derived from two Greek words – 'homoeos' (similar) and 'pathos' (disease). The principle is that the patient is given minute doses of a substance that, in a healthy person, would cause similar signs and symptoms. By creating a similar condition the homoeopathic remedy stimulates the body to heal itself. The skill lies in knowing the potency of the substances and matching them to the specific signs and symptom described by the patient. Treatments are prescribed individually to patients, who usually receive one high-potency dose of the remedy. Occasionally, symptoms may worsen but this is usually a short-term effect, an early stage of the healing process.

The remedies are prepared by repeatedly diluting plant and mineral extracts or substances that cause sensitivity (eg house dust). Unlike herbal medicine, in which only the direct effects of plants are used, homoeopathic remedies are designed to treat the whole person, not just the illness, so the person's overall physical and emotional state must be assessed. There are few diseases or conditions for which homoeopathy cannot be used, although there may still be the need for orthodox treatments. Homoeopathy cannot cure what is irreversible, and if long-term orthodox treatments have suppressed the body's natural powers these may take a while to regenerate. Homoeopathy is valuable in treating conditions such as high blood pressure, gout and insomnia, and can be given pre- and post-operatively to enhance healing.

For more *i*nformation

i To find your nearest homoeopathic practitioner, contact:

– Society of Homoeopaths (address on p 174);
– UK Homoeopathic Medical Association (address on p 175);
– British Homoeopathic Association (address on p 165).

i To find your nearest homoeopathic doctor, contact the Homoeopathic Trust (address on p 170).

i *The Family Encyclopaedia of Homoeopathic Remedies* by Dr Peter Webb, published by Robinson (or available from the British Homoeopathic Association: address on p 165).

i *People are Pets: Homoeopathy for first time users and their pets* by F Hunter and S Kayne, published by (and available from) the British Homoeopathic Association (address on p 165).

Reflexology

Keith

'I was doubtful about letting a therapist touch my feet because they are very sensitive but she convinced me that she wouldn't tickle. Once I settled down it really didn't feel uncomfortable and she was able to help my condition.'

Reflexology also complements orthodox medicine and involves massaging reflex areas in the body, found most commonly in the feet and hands, that correspond to all parts of the body. Practitioners believe that healing is encouraged by applying pressure to these points to free blockages in energy pathways. The reflex points are laid out to form a 'map' of the body, the right and left feet reflecting the right and left sides. A reflexologist takes a full history from the person and uses both feet to give whole body treatment. It's an ideal way to boost circulation.

The method has been used for several thousand years and is described in ancient Chinese and Egyptian writings. It does not claim to cure problems but therapists believe that many conditions respond well to reflexology, especially those related to stress – migraine, breathing disorders, and circulatory and digestive problems.

The practitioner will initially examine the feet for signs of the primary causes of conditions, which may originate from another system of the body, before moving on to precise massage. This involves applying firm pressure with the thumbs to all parts of the feet that correspond to the body areas giving problems. These related areas in the foot feel especially tender when massaged and the level of tenderness indicates the degree of imbalance in the body. The skill of the reflexologist lies in their ability to interpret the tenderness and apply the correct pressure, bearing in mind that some people have more sensitive feet than others. The number of treatments will vary according to the condition and the response. Reflexology is a relaxing therapy that relies on the healing power of touch rather than substances; at the end of each session people usually feel very warm and contented.

For more *i*nformation

ⓘ To find your nearest practitioner contact:

– Association of Reflexologists (address on p 164);
– International Federation of Reflexologists (address on p 171).

ⓘ *A Guide to Reflexology & Complementary Therapies*, published by Brockhampton Press.

ⓘ *Healing with Reflexology* by Rosalind Oxenford, published by Macmillan.

Meditation

Jenny

'I thought meditation sounded weird but, once I achieved the feeling of complete relaxation, I realised how calming the effect was on my whole body. My husband relies on me a lot, so I get up early to meditate and have a bit of time to myself.'

Meditation has a distinctly Eastern ring and is still used extensively as part of spiritual custom. People who practise meditation claim many benefits, ranging from reduction of stress through to increased mental ability. The capacity to concentrate the mind is an accomplished skill that will be an advantage in other areas of your life, and the relaxed state of mind it brings can help to reduce high blood pressure.

Before starting to meditate it is essential to have learnt to relax by more orthodox methods in order to achieve a tranquil state. The object is to attain a state of complete relaxation in mind and body by focusing thoughts on a single abstract image, article or word. Through this strict discipline the mind can be isolated from everyday worry and fear. Most people are content to reach and maintain this level of tranquillity, though others continue to search for greater spiritual awareness.

There are several types of meditation. Try the ones described here for a sufficient period of time to judge results and opt for the one that feels best. You and your relative can practise meditation together or alone.

The object you chose to concentrate on is not important. It can represent a view of a place with happy memories; a vision of colours; a treasured personal object; a word that has a special meaning; or you can 'listen' mentally to bars of music. The key to success is to switch off all external thoughts and concentrate on the object as a means of shutting out other intrusive thoughts and not to make judgements about what you are visualising. Although heightened 'transcendental' experiences may be your goal, initially you should be content to achieve an increased sense of well-being.

The value of meditation increases the more you practise. Make it a daily activity as a way to relax, or integrate the technique into everyday actions by focusing your senses on one task. A simple action such as washing your hands can have a calming effect if you concentrate enough on it.

Adopting the correct position

Poor posture is closely related to stress and is one of its contributing factors. Very constricted muscles send stress messages to the brain, exacerbating a tense, emotional state, and jangling nerves can push the body into a number of twisted positions. Think of the crossed legs and tightly hunched shoulder positions people adopt when trying to shut out external stress. Posture is important during meditation. The traditional poses include the lotus position from yoga, kneeling as in prayer or standing or sitting erect, but these positions are not vital if you or your relative find them difficult. Instead, choose a comfortable position, keeping the spine straight and try to remain still until you have finished. Achieving total immobility is part of the meditation process, so aching limbs may be an early drawback you will have to overcome.

Enhancing the mood

Set up an aromatherapy burner with a relaxing essential oil or burn a joss stick while meditating, as it helps to create a calming atmosphere. The basis of many joss sticks is frankincense, taken from the resin of a north African tree. It has a warm, balsamic aroma and is highly valued for its effects on the mind and the respiratory tract. Joss sticks can be bought readily in many high street shops and health stores.

Method one: concentration

The most basic and probably oldest type of meditation focuses on a single object. Adopt a sitting position with spine straight, head facing directly forward and eyes looking up towards brows or with eyelids closed. Breathe in a calm rhythm and begin to concentrate your mind in one of the following ways:

■ imagine a real object, a favourite picture or flower;
■ repeat a silent sound in your mind, or a low-pitched hum known as a *mantra* or incantation;
■ concentrate on an abstract thought such as peace or love;
■ concentrate on a part of the body such as the tip of the nose or the imagined back of the skull.

Traditionally a mantra would have had a religious meaning but this is not necessary for your chosen words. Any thought that focuses your mind will work well. Dwell on this object calmly, push away intrusive thoughts and keep drawing the mind back to the object. Initially, other thoughts will creep in every few seconds, but with discipline the time span can be lengthened until minutes pass without distraction. Ten minutes is ideal but a few minutes are sufficient to restore peace and reduce anxiety. The feeling of relaxation is produced through the mind's repetition of sound or thought. When the meditation is completed, stretch your body and bring it gently back to the everyday world. Practised meditators have been subjected to very strong physical sensations while in deep meditation without showing any effects on their levels of concentration.

Other methods

A number of other similar methods can be used, all variations on the concentration technique.

■ **Your corner of heaven** This takes the theme of visiting a happy place a stage further. Because you visit this place often in your meditation, you should be able to step in and out of it at will. If it is a room, you can change the decoration; if it is a garden you can change the nature of the plants and smell the scents. It creates a safe place for you to enter at times of stress and eases meditation because it uses a range of senses rather than a single focus.

■ **Tactile meditation** As the name suggests, this method uses touch. Choose a few pebbles or a set of worry beads and move them from hand to hand. As you move each pebble or bead, feel it and count it. Keep the movement rhythmical and repetitive.

■ **Tratak** With this Indian form of meditation you concentrate on a real lighted candle until your eyes water, then you close your eyes and the image is retained in your mind.

For more *i*nformation

i To find your nearest practitioner, contact the Buddhist Society (address on p 165).

i *Teach Yourself Meditation* by Naomi Ozaniec, published by Hodder & Stoughton.

i *Meditation* by Erica Smith and Nicholas Wilkes, published by Vermilion.

i *The Complete Meditation Kit* (containing book, tape, cards and candle) by C Devereaux, published by Piatkus.

Visualisation

Jenny

'When my husband could no longer go out for a walk, I would say to him "let's go for a walk together along the cliffs" and we would shut our eyes and walk for miles in our minds. It gave us so much pleasure, we could almost smell the sea.'

Visualisation is a method similar to meditation but it needs much less concentration and is easier to perform. It works well whether it's done alone or with someone else. Therapists use visualisation as a healing exercise to help lift the effects of depression and to create a positive attitude towards life-threatening illnesses; it can have powerful psychological effects. It is believed that visualisation influences the brain centres that control hormone and immune systems and helps to strengthen the healing process. Using it at home is an excellent way to shut out other stressful thoughts and to mentally take yourself somewhere pleasant. The technique works by creating a sense of contentment and pleasure so that the brain responds to this lack of threat by telling the systems of the body to go into rest rather than alert mode. If you try thinking unpleasant thoughts, you will feel the reverse happen: as you think about a difficult situation, the body immediately responds by rousing itself for action, even though the event is imagined. This action will show you how quickly discomforting thoughts can be subdued by replacing them with happier images. Enjoy these extended forms of relaxation alone or with your relative, and hold on to the sense of pleasure and calm for as long as you can.

First you need to sit or lie comfortably in a quiet place. If you are with a partner, decide whether you want to 'visit' somewhere you both know or one person will take the other on a 'guided' tour using a reading similar to the one below. The guided journey takes five to ten minutes after you have spent some time relaxing.

Guided visualisation

To enjoy the experience, you need to be guided through a journey by another person, who reads from a script or tells a story, or you can use a recorded tape if you are alone. The point of the exercise is to follow a set of visual images through pleasant surroundings to a destination and then slowly retrace your steps back to the real world. If unwelcome thoughts creep in, put them aside and continue with the journey. You can write your own journey – real or fantasy or base it on a painting that you both like. Try the exercise overleaf as an example journey.

Close your eyes. You are sitting in a chair in the garden of a house where you have spent many happy summer holidays. The sun is shining and you are relaxing with a cup of morning coffee and a newspaper. For a while you listen to the sound of the birds and the insects droning in the flowers. You stretch your legs, get up from the chair and walk down the gravel path towards the old gate. The path is winding and is lined by a sweet smelling border of summer flowers.

You open the gate and walk out into a shady lane. The dappled sun is pleasantly warm and you set off on a favourite walk. The lane winds gently down hill and, as you walk along, sounds reach you from across the fields. Children are playing and a skylark is calling. The lane turns a corner and opens quite suddenly to reveal the horizon – in the distance you can just define the line where the hazy blue of the sky meets the darker blue of the sea. Closer to land, the sea is a lighter shade of blue that takes on many tones of green above the sand. The cliffs are high and made of dark granite.

This walk is well known to you but it never fails to please. You reach the low stone wall with its tamarisk hedge and pass through the gap to the path along the cliff. Here the breeze catches your hair, the smell of sea is strong and the sound of seagulls audible overhead. You follow the path and make for the headland. Slightly puffed from the wind and the exercise, you sit for a while to watch the sea in its search for continuous motion and marvel yet again at the view.

Rested, you close your eyes briefly to store the vista in your mind. You reach to touch a clump of sea pinks with their wiry stems before standing up to retrace your steps. You return along the cliff path and smell the tamarisk as you slip back into the quiet lane. You walk slowly back up the sandy road until you see the house through the trees. You unlatch the gate and walk back down the garden path to rest again in the wicker chair, with time before lunch to think about the pleasant experience that you will repeat again tomorrow.

It is time to bring the journey to an end, so, in your own time, open your eyes, stretch your limbs and start to think about the present.

Other therapies

There are many other types of alternative therapies that can be used to complement each other and orthodox medicine. You can find out more about them at your local library:

- Chiropractic – relieves pain through joint manipulation.
- Flotation therapy – relieves stress through floating on very buoyant water in a light- and sound-proofed tank.
- Herbal medicine – uses the potent healing properties of plants. Note that these preparations must always be used with caution; like all drugs, they can have unwanted (side) effects.
- Hypnotherapy – induces a trance-like state to bring about physical and mental changes.
- Hydrotherapy – water treatments to purify and heal the body.
- Osteopathy – manipulative therapy used widely in orthodox medicine.
- T'ai-chi Ch'uan – meditation in motion.

Conclusion

There is a wide range of alternative therapies available. Many, such as aromatherapy and reflexology, aim to treat the whole body whilst others, such as osteopathy, are used for more specific problems. You and your relative may be sceptical about whether they work, especially if they rely on less orthodox and 'unseen' methods. No therapist or practitioner of alternative therapies will ever claim to 'cure' a patient or to replace orthodox medicine, but they will strongly support the notion that their treatments can contribute towards the healing process. People who use a qualified practitioner can expect to receive more time for treatment, a whole body approach to their problems and advice about self-help. If your relative's health is failing, it's well worth considering some of these treatments alongside orthodox medicine, as they can bring tremendous relief from distress and discomfort. A word of caution – it is always wise to consult with your own medical doctor first.

For more *i*nformation

i The following organisations will give you advice and supply you with further details of specialist organisations (addresses in the 'Useful addresses' section at the end of the book):

- Centre for Study of Complementary Medicine;
- Council for Complementary and Alternative Medicine;
- General Council & Register of Osteopaths;
- Hale Clinic;
- Institute of Complementary Medicine;
- National Federation of Spiritual Healers;
- Society for the Promotion of Nutritional Therapy.

i *Reader's Digest Family Guide to Alternative Medicine*, published by Reader's Digest.

i *What's the Alternative?* by Hazel Courteney, published by Infinity Press (PO Box 4629, Edgbaston, Birmingham B15 3TW).

Useful addresses

Accountant of Court
2 Parliament House
Edinburgh EH1 1RQ
Tel: 0131-225 2595
For information about applying for the appointment of a curator bonis.

AidCall plc
Freepost (EX2356)
Newton Abbot
Devon TQ13 7BR
Tel: 0345 413103
Provides a 24-hour emergency response service.

Across Trust
Bridge House
70–72 Bridge Road
East Molesey
Surrey KT8 9HF
Tel: 0181-783 1355
Provides accompanied holidays and pilgrimages for sick and disabled people by means of a jumbo-ambulance.

Air Transport Users Council
5th Floor
Kingsway House
103 Kingsway
London WC2B 6QX
Tel: 0171-242 3882
Publishes a booklet Flight Plan, *which has a section for disabled passengers.*

Aromatherapy Organisation Council
PO Box 355
Croydon
Surrey CR9 2QP
Tel: 0181-251 7912
For a list of qualified practitioners in your area.

Association of Reflexologists
27 Old Gloucester Street
London WC1N 3XX
Tel: 0990 673320
For names of reflexologists.

Bach Centre
Mount Vernon Ltd
Bakers Lane
Sotwell
Wallingford
Oxfordshire OX10 0PX
Tel: 01491 834678
For list of trained practitioners and details of publications, tapes and educational material.

BNA (British Nursing Association)
North Place
82 Great North Road
Hatfield
Hertfordshire AL9 5BL
Tel: 01707 263544
For respite care.

British Association for Counselling
1 Regent Place
Rugby
Warwickshire CV21 2PJ
Tel: 01788 578328
Publishes a directory of counsellors in the UK.

British Heart Foundation
14 Fitzhardinge Street
London W1H 4DH
Tel: 0171-935 0185
Publishes the Heart Information Series – a range of booklets on all problems and treatments relating to heart disease.

British Homoeopathic Association
27a Devonshire Street
London W1N 1RJ
Tel: 0171-935 2163
For the names of homoeopathic practitioners.

British Red Cross
9 Grosvenor Crescent
London SW1X 7EJ
Tel: 0171-235 5454
Or look in the telephone directory for a contact number.
For advice about arranging for equipment on loan.

Buddhist Society
58 Ecclestone Square
London SW1L 1PH
Tel: 0171-834 5858
For information about practitioners of meditation.

Care and Repair
Castle House
Kirtley Drive
Nottingham NG7 1LD
Tel: 0115-070 9091
Advice and practical assistance to older and disabled people and those on low incomes, to help them improve their home conditions.

Carers National Association
20–25 Glasshouse Yard
London EC1A 4JS
Tel: 0171-490 8818
CarersLine: 0345 573 369 (Mon to Fri, 10 am–noon and 2–4 pm)
Acts as the national voice of carers, raising awareness and providing support, information and advice.

Centre for Study of Complementary Medicine
51 Bedford Place
Southampton SO1 2DG
Tel: 01703 334752
For advice and details of specialist organisations.

Chest, Heart and Stroke Scotland
65 North Castle Street
Edinburgh EH2 3LT
Tel: 0131-225 6963
For information and advice about caring for someone with a heart problem.

Community Transport Association
Highbank
Halton Street
Hyde
Cheshire SK14 2NY
Tel: 0161-351 1475
Advice: 0161-367 8780
Services to benefit providers of transport for people with mobility problems.

Coronary Prevention Group
42 Store Street
London WC1E 7DB
Tel: 0171-580 1070
Provides a range of information leaflets, newsletter and reading list.

Council for Complementary and Alternative Medicine
179 Gloucester Place
London NW1 6DX
Tel: 0171-724 9103
Advice and details of specialist organisations.

Counsel and Care
Lower Ground Floor
Twyman House
16 Bonny Street
London NW1 9PG
Tel: 0171-485 1566
Offers free counselling, information and advice for older people and carers, including specialist advice about using independent agencies and the administration of trust funds for single payments (eg respite care).

Crossroads Care
10 Regent Place
Rugby
Warwickshire CV21 2PN
Tel: 01788 573653
For respite care.

Dial-a-Ride (DART)
Unit 11
Spectrum House
32–34 Gordon House Road
London NW5 1LP
Tel: 0171-482 2325
Information about local dial-a-ride and taxicard schemes.

Disability Living Centres Council
Winchester House
11 Cranmer Road
London SW9 6EJ
Tel: 0171-820 0567
For the Disability Living Centre nearest you, where you can see aids and equipment.

Disability Scotland
Princes House
5 Shandwick Place
Edinburgh EH2 4RG
Tel: 0131-229 8632
For information on non-medical aspects of disability.

Disabled Living Foundation
380–384 Harrow Road
London W9 2HU
Tel: 0171-289 6111
Equipment helpline: 0870 603 9177
Minicom: 0879 603 9176
Information and advice about all aspects of daily living (and aids) for people with disability.

Disabled Persons Railcard Office
PO Box 1YT
Newcastle-upon-Tyne NE99 1YT
Helpline: 0191-269 0303
For a railcard offering concessionary fares. An application form and useful booklet called Rail Travel for Disabled Passengers *can be found at most stations or from the address above.*

Drinkline
7th Floor
Weddell House
13–14 Smithfield
London EC1A 9DL
Tel: 0171-332 0202
National alcohol helpline that provides confidential information, help and advice about drinking to anyone, including people worried about someone else's drinking.

Elderly Accommodation Council
46a Chiswick High Road
London W4 1SZ
Tel: 0181-995 8320
Helpline: 0181-742 1181
Computerised information about all forms of accommodation for older people (including nursing homes and hospices) and advice on top-up funding.

Family Heart Association
7 North Road
Maidenhead
Berkshire SL6 1PL
Tel: 01628 628 638
Information on coronary heart disease and its management.

Federation of Independent Advice Centres
4 Dean's Court
St Paul's Churchyard
London EC4V 5AA
Tel: 0171-489 1800
Promotes the provision of independent advice services in the UK.

General Council & Register of Osteopaths
56 London Street
Reading
Berkshire RG1 4SQ
Tel: 0118-957 6585
Advice and details of specialist organisations.

Hale Clinic
7 Park Crescent
London W1N 3HE
Tel: 0171-631 0156
For advice and details of specialist organisations.

Health Education Authority
Hamilton House
Mabledon Place
London WC1H 9TX
Tel: 0171-383 3833
Provides details of a wide range of leaflets and books promoting good health.

Help the Aged
16–18 St James's Walk
London EC1R 0BE
Tel: 0171-253 0253
SeniorLine: 0800 65 00 65
SeniorLink: 01483 773952
Advice and support for older people and their carers.

HELPBOX
The Help for Health Trust
Freepost
Winchester SO22 5BR
Tel: 01962 849 100
A computer database that holds a vast and comprehensive range of health-related information.

Holiday Care Service
2nd Floor
Imperial Buildings
Victoria Road
Horley
Surrey RH6 7PZ
Tel: 01293 774535
Textphone: 01293 776943
Information and advice on holidays, travel facilities and respite care available for people with disabilities, on low income or with special needs.

Homoeopathic Trust
2 Powis Place
Great Ormond Street
London WC1N 3HT
Tel: 0171-837 9469
For the names of homoeopathic doctors.

Hospice Information Service
St Christopher's Hospice
51–59 Lawrie Park Road
London SE26 6DZ
Tel: 0181-778 9252
For information about hospices and hospice care.

Independent Healthcare Association
22 Little Russell Street
London WC1A 2HT
Tel: 0171-430 0837
For information about finding and paying for residential and nursing home care.

Independent Living (1993) Fund
PO Box 183
Nottingham NG8 3RD
Tel: 0115-942 8191
May fund very severely disabled people to buy in extra care if there is no one to fully meet their care needs.

Institute of Complementary Medicine
PO Box 194
London SE16 1QZ
Tel: 0171-237 5165
Advice and details of specialist organisations.

International Federation of Aromatherapists
Stamford House
2–4 Chiswick Road
London W4 1TH
Tel: 0181-742 2605
For a list of qualified practitioners in your area.

International Federation of Reflexologists
78 Edridge Road
Croydon
Surrey CR0 1EF
Tel: 0181-667 9458
For names of reflexologists.

International Society of Professional Aromatherapists
The Annexe
Hinckley & District Hospital
Hinckley
Leicestershire LE10 1AG
Tel: 01455 637987
For a list of qualified practitioners in your area.

Jewish Care
Stewart Young House
221 Golders Green Road
London NW11 9DQ
Tel: 0181-458 3282
Social care, personal support and residential homes for Jewish people.

Motability
Gate House, West Gate
Harlow
Essex CM20 1HR
Helpline: 01279 635 666
Advice and help about cars, scooters and wheelchairs for disabled people.

National Association of Councils for Voluntary Service
3rd Floor, Arundel Court
177 Arundel Street
Sheffield S1 2NU
Tel: 0114-278 6636
Promotes and supports the work of councils for voluntary service.

National Association of Volunteer Bureaux
New Oxford House
16 Waterloo Street
Birmingham B2 5UG
Tel: 0121-633 4555
Information on matters related to volunteering, with a directory of volunteer bureaux and other publications.

National Federation of Spiritual Healers
Old Manor Farm Studio
Church Street
Sunbury on Thames
Middlesex TW16 6RG
Tel: 0891 616 080 (premium rate line)
Advice and details of specialist organisations.

New World Aurora
16a Neal's Yard
Covent Garden
London WC2H 9DP
Tel: 0171-379 5972
For catalogue of relaxation music tapes.

Public Trust Office
Protection Division
Stewart House
24 Kingsway
London WC2B 6JX
Tel: 0171-664 7300/7208
Advice about powers of attorney.

Quitline
Tel: 0800 002 200
A freephone helpline that provides confidential and practical advice for people wanting to give up smoking.

RADAR (Royal Association for Disability and Rehabilitation)
12 City Forum
250 City Road
London EC1V 8AF
Tel: 0171-250 3222
Information about aids and mobility, holidays and leisure.

Register for Qualified Aromatherapists
23 Castle Street
Tiverton
Devon EX16 6RE
Tel: 01884 243172
For a list of qualified practitioners in your area.

Relaxation for Living Trust
12 New Street
Chipping Norton
Oxfordshire OX7 5LJ
Tel: 01608 646 100
Publishes a range of materials to help reduce stress.

Research Institute for Consumer Affairs (RICA)
2 Marylebone Road
London NW1 4DF
Tel/Textphone: 0171-830 7508
Fax: 0171-830 7679
Tests and evaluates goods and services for disabled and older people, including ordinary consumer products as well as special aids and equipment.

Royal College of Psychiatrists
17 Belgrave Square
London SW1X 8PG
Tel: 0171-235 2351
Publishes a range of leaflets for dealing with anxieties, phobias, depression and bereavement (send a sae with request).

St John Ambulance
Look in the telephone directory for a contact number.
For advice about arranging for equipment on loan.

Shen Tao Foundation
Middle Piccadilly Natural Healing Centre
Holwell
Dorset DT9 5LW
Tel: 01963 23468
To find a practitioner in your area. Please enclose sae when requesting information.

Society for the Promotion of Nutritional Therapy
PO Box 47
Heathfield
East Sussex TN21 9ZX
Tel: 01435 867007
Advice and details of specialist organisations.

Society of Homoeopaths
2 Artizan Road
Northampton NN1 4HU
Tel: 01604 621 400
For the names of homoeopathic practitioners.

Special Families Home Swap Register
Erme House
Station Road
Plympton
Plymouth PL7 3BR
Tel: 01752 347577
Produces a quarterly register to enable physically disabled people to swap their home for breaks elsewhere in the country.

SPOD (Association to Aid the Sexual and Personal Relationships of People with a Disability)
286 Camden Road
London N7 0BJ
Tel: 0171-607 8851
Telephone counselling Monday and Wednesday 1.30–4.30 pm and Tuesday and Thursday 10.30 am–1.30 pm.

Sports Council
16 Upper Woburn Place
London WC1H 0QP
Tel: 0171-263 1500
Provides general information about all sports.

174

Stress Management Training Institute
Foxhills
30 Victoria Avenue
Shanklin
Isle of Wight PO37 6LS
Tel: 01983 868 166
Publishes a wide range of materials to help reduce stress: leaflets, audio tapes, books and a newsletter.

Stroke Association
123–127 Whitecross Street
London EC1Y 8JJ
Tel: 0171-490 7999 (1.00–3.55 pm)
Information and advice about chest, heart and stroke illnesses.

Tripscope
The Courtyard
Evelyn Road
London W4 5JL
Tel/Textphone: 0345 585 641
A travel and transport information service for older and disabled people in London and the southwest.

UK College for Complementary Health Care Studies
St Charles Hospital
Exmoor Street
London W10 6DZ
Tel: 0181-964 1205
For a list of qualified practitioners of therapeutic massage.

UK Homoeopathic Medical Association
6 Livingstone Road
Gravesend
Kent DA12 5DZ
Tel: 01474 560336
For the names of homoeopathic practitioners.

United Kingdom Home Care Association (UKHCA)
42 Banstead Road
Carshalton Beeches
Surrey SM5 3NW
Tel: 0181-288 1551
For information about organisations providing home care in your area.

University of the Third Age (U3A)
National Office
26 Harrison Street
London WC1H 8JG
Tel: 0171-837 8838
Day-time study and recreational classes. Send an sae for further information about classes for older people, or look in the telephone directory for local branch.

Vehicle Excise Duty (Road Tax)
DLA Unit
Warbreck House
Warbreck Hill Road
Blackpool FY2 0YE
Tel: 01345 123456
Information about exemption from road tax for vehicles used exclusively by or for disabled people.

Winged Fellowship
Angel House
20–32 Pentonville Road
London N1 9XD
Tel: 0171-833 2594
Provides respite care and holidays for physically disabled people, with or without a partner.

About Age Concern

Caring for someone with a heart problem is one of a wide range of publications produced by Age Concern England, the National Council on Ageing. Age Concern cares about all older people and believes later life should be fulfilling and enjoyable. For too many this is impossible. As the leading charitable movement in the UK concerned with ageing and older people, Age Concern finds effective ways to change that situation.

Where possible, we enable older people to solve problems themselves, providing as much or as little support as they need. Our network of 1,400 local groups, supported by 250,000 volunteers, provides community-based services such as lunch clubs, day centres and home visiting.

Nationally, we take a lead role campaigning, parliamentary work, policy analysis, research, specialist information and advice provision, and publishing. Innovative programmes promote healthier life-styles and provide older people with opportunities to give the experience of a lifetime back to their communities.

Age Concern is dependent on donations, covenants and legacies.

Age Concern England
1268 London Road
London SW16 4ER
Tel: 0181-765 7200

Age Concern Scotland
113 Rose Street
Edinburgh EH2 3DT
Tel: 0131-220 3345

Age Concern Cymru
4th Floor
1 Cathedral Road
Cardiff CF1 9SD
Tel: 01222 371566

Age Concern Northern Ireland
3 Lower Crescent
Belfast BT7 1NR
Tel: 01232 245729

Other books in this series

Choices for the carer of an elderly relative
Marina Lewycka
Being a carer may mean many different things – from living at a distance and keeping a check on things by telephone to taking on full-time caring role. This book looks at the choices facing someone whose parent or other relative needs care. It helps readers to look at their own circumstances and their own priorities and decide what is the best role for themselves – as well as the person being cared for.
£6.99   0–86242–263–9

Caring for someone who has dementia
Jane Brotchie
Caring for someone with dementia can be physically and emotionally exhausting, and it is often difficult to think about what can be done to make the situation easier. This book shows how to cope better and seek further help as well as containing detailed information on the illness itself and what to expect in the future.
£6.99   0–86242–259–0

Caring for someone who is dying
Penny Mares
Confronting the knowledge that a loved one is going to die soon is always a moment of crisis. And the pain of the news can be compounded by the need to take responsibility for the care and support given in the last months and weeks. This book attempts to help readers cope with their emotions, identify the needs that the situation creates and make the practical arrangements necessary to ensure that the passage through the period is as smooth as possible.
£6.99   0–86242–260–4

The Carer's Handbook: What to do and who to turn to
Marina Lewycka
At some point in their lives millions of people find themselves suddenly responsible for organising the care of an older person with a health crisis. All too often such carers have no idea what services are available or who can be approached for support. This book is designed to act as a first point of reference in just such an emergency, signposting readers to many more detailed, local sources of advice.
£6.99   0–86242–262–0

Caring for someone who has had a stroke
Philip Coyne and Penny Mares
Although 100,000 people in Britain will have a stroke this year, many people are still confused about what stroke actually means. This book is designed to help carers understand stroke and its immediate aftermath. It contains extensive information on hospital discharge, providing care, rehabilitation and adjustment to life at home.
£6.99   0–86242–264–7

Caring for someone with alcohol problems
Mike Ward
When drinking becomes a problem, the consequences for the carer can be physically and emotionally exhausting. This book will help anyone who lives with or cares for a problem drinker, with particular emphasis on caring for an older problem drinker.
£6.99   0–86242–227–2

Caring for someone at a distance
Julie Spencer-Cingöz
With people now living longer, sooner or later we are likely to find ourselves looking after a loved one or a friend – often at a distance. This book will help you to identify the needs and priorities that have to be addressed, offering guidance on the key decisions to be made, minimising risks, what to look for when you visit, how to get the most out of your visits, dealing with your relative's finances and keeping in touch.
£6.99   0–86242–228–0

Publications from Age Concern Books

Health and care

Know Your Medicines, 3rd edition
Pat Blair

A handy guide to medicines in older age, this book answers the key questions older people might want to know about their medicines and how to use them.

Updated, revised, and now in its third edition, this popular guide explains many of the common questions older people – and those who care for them – may have about the medicines they use and how these can affect them. Clearly written, and avoiding unnecessary jargon, it covers:

- how medicines actually work
- using medicines more effectively
- getting advice and asking questions
- side effects
- medicines and your body systems
- common ailments

There is also information about the dosage and strength of medicines, brands, the storage and disposal of medicines, and an index to help look up medicines that are prescribed or bought 'over the counter'. This new edition will serve as a valuable source of advice and guidance.

£7.99   0–86242–226–4

Money matters

Your Rights: A guide to money benefits for older people
Sally West

Written in clear and concise language, *Your Rights* guides readers through the maze of money benefits for older people and explains what you can claim and why. Specific sections are provided on:

■ Retirement pensions
■ Housing and Council Tax Benefit
■ Benefits for disabled people
■ Income Support and the Social Fund
■ Paying for residential care
■ Help with legal and health costs

For further information, please ring 0181-765 7200.

Managing Other People's Money, 2nd edition
Penny Letts

It is difficult enough looking after our own money, let alone managing someone else's. Fully revised and updated, this new edition examines just when such a need might arise and provides a step-by-step guide to the arrangements that have to be made. Adopting a clear and concise approach, topics include:

■ when to take over
■ the powers available
■ what needs to be done
■ enduring power of attorney
■ the Court of Protection

Other areas covered include claiming benefits, collecting pensions and salaries, living arrangements and residential care. Ideal both for the family carer and for legal and other advice workers, this new edition is essential reading for anyone facing this challenging situation.

£9.99   0–86242–250–7

If you would like to order any of these titles, please write to the address below, enclosing a cheque or money order for the appropriate amount made payable to Age Concern England. Credit card orders may be made on 0181-765 7200.

Mail Order Unit
Age Concern England
1268 London Road
London SW16 4ER

Information Line

Age Concern produces over 40 comprehensive factsheets designed to answer many of the questions older people – or those advising them – may have, on topics such as:

- finding and paying for residential and nursing home care
- money benefits
- finding help at home
- legal affairs
- making a will
- help with heating
- raising income from your home
- transfer of assets

Age Concern offers a factsheet subscription service that presents all the factsheets in a folder, together with regular updates throughout the year. The first year's subscription currently costs £50; renewal thereafter is £25.

To order your FREE factsheet list, phone 0800 00 99 66 (a free call) or write to:

Age Concern
FREEPOST (SWB 30375)
Ashburton
Devon TQ13 7ZZ

Index